CHARLES DARWIN

AND THE ORIGIN OF SPECIES

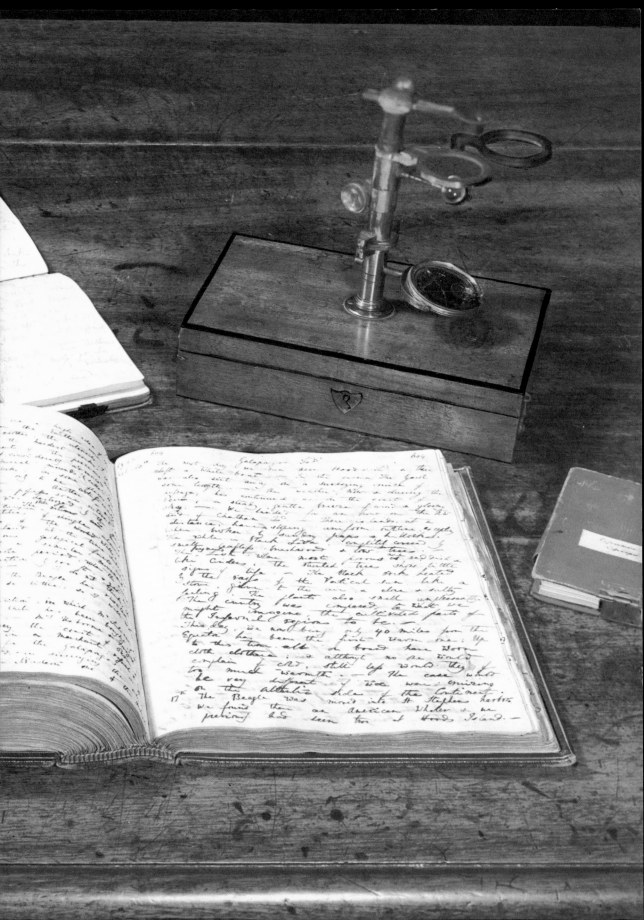

There are a number of HORIZON CARAVEL BOOKS published each year. Titles now available are:

CHARLES DARWIN AND THE ORIGIN OF SPECIES
RUSSIA IN REVOLUTION
DESERT WAR IN NORTH AFRICA
THE BATTLE OF WATERLOO
THE HOLY LAND IN THE TIME OF JESUS
THE SPANISH ARMADA
BUILDING THE SUEZ CANAL
MOUNTAIN CONQUEST
PHARAOHS OF EGYPT
LEONARDO DA VINCI
THE FRENCH REVOLUTION
CORTES AND THE AZTEC CONQUEST
CAESAR
THE UNIVERSE OF GALILEO AND NEWTON
THE VIKINGS
MARCO POLO'S ADVENTURES IN CHINA
SHAKESPEARE'S ENGLAND
CAPTAIN COOK AND THE SOUTH PACIFIC
THE SEARCH FOR EARLY MAN
JOAN OF ARC
EXPLORATION OF AFRICA
NELSON AND THE AGE OF FIGHTING SAIL
ALEXANDER THE GREAT
RUSSIA UNDER THE CZARS
HEROES OF POLAR EXPLORATION
KNIGHTS OF THE CRUSADES

American Heritage also publishes AMERICAN HERITAGE JUNIOR LIBRARY books, a similar series on American history. Titles now available are:

TO THE PACIFIC WITH LEWIS AND CLARK
THEODORE ROOSEVELT, THE STRENUOUS LIFE
GEORGE WASHINGTON AND THE MAKING OF A NATION
CAPTAINS OF INDUSTRY
CARRIER WAR IN THE PACIFIC
JAMESTOWN: FIRST ENGLISH COLONY
AMERICANS IN SPACE
ABRAHAM LINCOLN IN PEACE AND WAR
AIR WAR AGAINST HITLER'S GERMANY
IRONCLADS OF THE CIVIL WAR
THE ERIE CANAL
THE MANY WORLDS OF BENJAMIN FRANKLIN
COMMODORE PERRY IN JAPAN
THE BATTLE OF GETTYSBURG
ANDREW JACKSON, SOLDIER AND STATESMAN
ADVENTURES IN THE WILDERNESS
LEXINGTON, CONCORD AND BUNKER HILL
CLIPPER SHIPS AND CAPTAINS
D-DAY, THE INVASION OF EUROPE
WESTWARD ON THE OREGON TRAIL
THE FRENCH AND INDIAN WARS
GREAT DAYS OF THE CIRCUS
STEAMBOATS ON THE MISSISSIPPI
COWBOYS AND CATTLE COUNTRY
TEXAS AND THE WAR WITH MEXICO
THE PILGRIMS AND PLYMOUTH COLONY
THE CALIFORNIA GOLD RUSH
PIRATES OF THE SPANISH MAIN
TRAPPERS AND MOUNTAIN MEN
MEN OF SCIENCE AND INVENTION
NAVAL BATTLES AND HEROES
THOMAS JEFFERSON AND HIS WORLD
DISCOVERERS OF THE NEW WORLD
RAILROADS IN THE DAYS OF STEAM
INDIANS OF THE PLAINS
THE STORY OF YANKEE WHALING

A HORIZON CARAVEL BOOK

CHARLES DARWIN

AND THE ORIGIN OF SPECIES

By the Editors of
HORIZON MAGAZINE

Author
WALTER KARP

Consultant
DR. J. W. BURROW
Lecturer in History, University of East Anglia

Published by American Heritage Publishing Co., Inc.
Book Trade and Institutional Distribution by
Harper & Row

FIRST EDITION
Library of Congress Catalog Card Number: 68–12439
© 1968 by American Heritage Publishing Co., Inc., 551 Fifth Avenue, New
York, New York 10017. All rights reserved under Berne and Pan-American Copyright Conventions.
Trademark CARAVEL registered United States Patent Office

Darwin did most of his research at this small desk in the window of his study, now preserved, like the rest of Down House, as a memorial to him.

FOREWORD

Few scientists have shared Charles Darwin's gift of perception, of analyzing the everyday world around him with fresh and penetrating eyes. Still fewer have had his open-minded willingness to set aside preconceptions in order to test a revolutionary idea. Darwin's theory of evolution by natural selection—as put forth in his epochal 1859 work *The Origin of Species*—shocked the world of mid-nineteenth-century science, a world that was accustomed to explaining all puzzling facts about nature as being the actions of an omniscient Creator. Initially, belief in "Darwinism" was equated with blasphemy and atheism, an attitude that has lingered on in parts of the United States until very recently.

To Darwin himself the religious issue was never a problem. He was a deeply moral man but—although once destined for the ministry—not a profoundly religious one. The furor his work caused amazed him. To him recognition of evolution by natural selection seemed in no way incompatible with belief in God as Prime Mover of the universe, nor has it, in fact, proved to be so for succeeding generations of scientists and laymen.

The twentieth-century view of science, indeed, is so firmly founded on evolution that it is hard today to understand how monstrous a blow the first revelation of Darwin's theory struck at most scientists' reputations, as well as at their religious convictions. It took the genius of men like Thomas Huxley, Joseph Hooker, and Charles Lyell—respectively England's leading zoologist, botanist, and geologist, and all, fortunately, Darwin's friends—to perceive how the theory of evolution made sense out of chaos and to begin gradually applying it to their own work.

Since Darwin's day, advances in the study of heredity, mutations, and genetics have uncovered errors in his theory, some of them gaps that Darwin himself suspected but could not fill, given the state of knowledge at the time. But his basic principle of natural selection has emerged triumphant. As Thomas Huxley's grandson, the distinguished biologist Sir Julian Huxley, has expressed it: "Not only is natural selection inevitable, not only is it *an* effective agency of evolution, but it is *the* only effective agency of evolution."

THE EDITORS

7

RIGHT: *To avoid offending Victorian morality, the* Beagle's *artist depicted a skin-clad Fuegian wearing considerably more covering than usual.*

COVER: *At thirty-one, Darwin had outlined a theory that would banish such concepts of creation as Breughel's Garden of Eden, behind him.*

FRONT ENDSHEET: *Field notebooks, telescope, microscope, and Darwin's manuscript* Journal *record his industry during the long* Beagle *voyage.*

TITLE PAGE: *A 1958 Linnean Society medal commemorates the centennial of the first reading of Darwin's early outline of his theory of evolution.*

BACK ENDSHEET: *Darwin's specimens from the* Beagle *trip include beetles (left), birds, an armadillo (center), and many huge fossil bones.*

BACK COVER: *The zoologist who classified Darwin's South American bird specimens named this fruit-eating* Tanagra darwini *after the scientist.*

CONTENTS

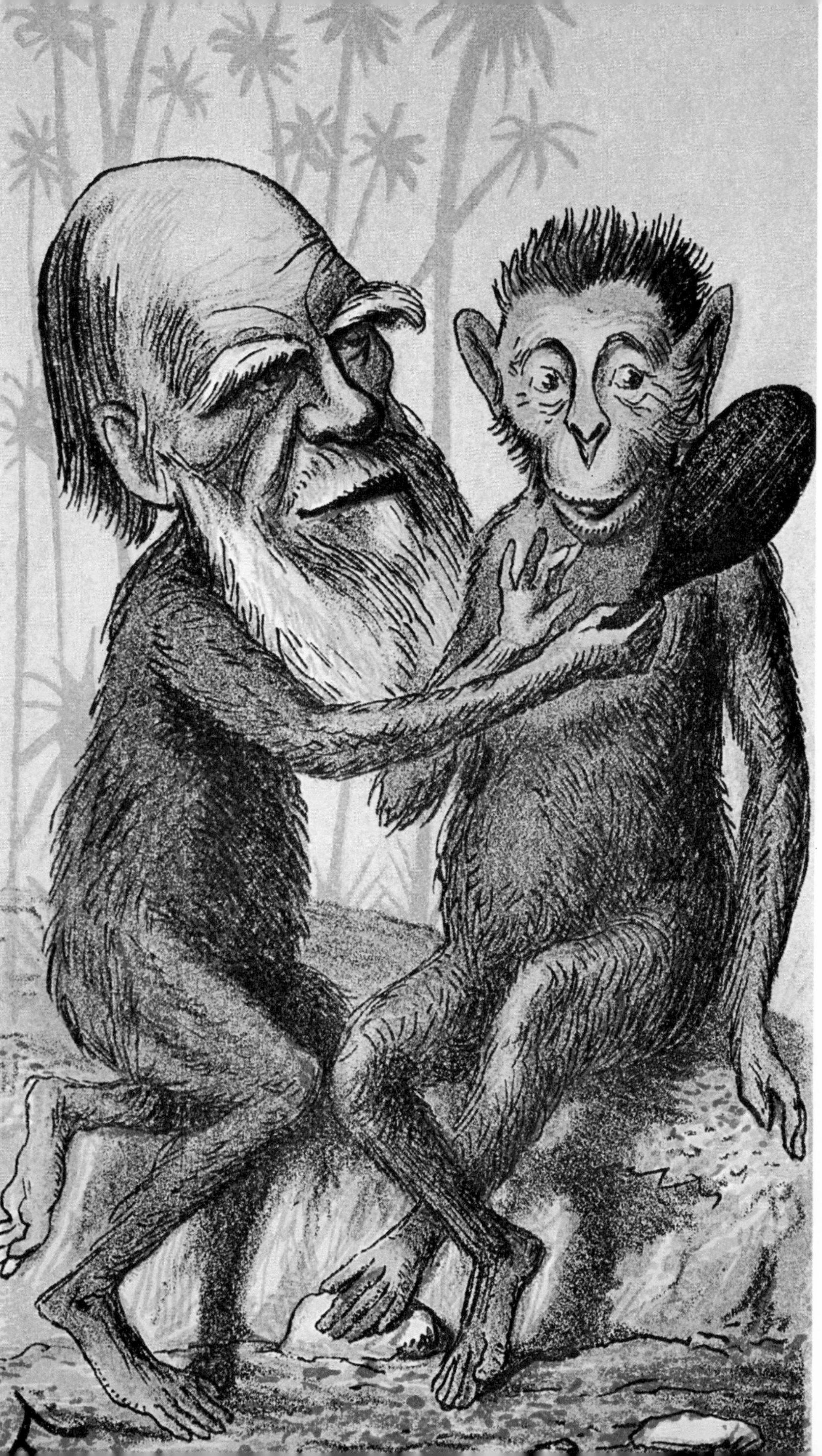

I

IN SEARCH OF A CAREER

In the year 1859 a great event occurred in England that sent shock waves across the world. It was not an outbreak of war—although men said it would destroy all that they most cherished. It was not some great epidemic, or a terrible earthquake, or a violent revolution—although people discussed it as if it were all of these things. The event was the publication of a book with an extremely long title: *The Origin of Species by Means of Natural Selection, or the Preservation of Favoured Races in the Struggle for Life.* Its author was a fifty-year-old country gentleman named Charles Darwin, who believed that he had discovered a great truth about living things. It was so new, so incredible, and it so completely upset established ways of thought that for twenty years he had kept it to himself, confiding only in a few scientific friends in England and the United States. The idea he set forth in his book was the theory of evolution by natural selection.

According to this theory, the myriad species, or individual types, of living things that inhabit the earth are all descended from a few, much simpler, ancient species, which gradually evolved, or changed, over the course of millions of years. Not only had they changed, said Darwin; they had changed entirely by natural means. The lion and the horse, the soaring eagle and the lowly lobster were not, by Darwin's theory, the special, individual handiwork of the Creator, as men had long believed. Instead, all species of living things had developed solely through the working of a certain natural process that Darwin had discovered and now revealed in his book.

Such was Darwin's doctrine, and in all the history of science no theory was ever so instantly and savagely at-

A British cartoonist satirized Charles Darwin's controversial theory of evolution by depicting the bearded scientist as a shaggy monkey, holding a mirror in which the delighted ape can see his close resemblance to man.

The corpulent Dr. Robert Waring Darwin, Charles' father, looked out upon a comfortable world with great satisfaction. Robert's wife, Susannah, sat for the miniature portrait below at the age of 27.

tacked. In the months that followed the publication of his book, men of science and men of the church rose up united against it. An article in the *Quarterly Review* for July, 1860, called Darwin a flighty man who had written an "utterly rotten fabric of guess and speculation." The distinguished Harvard naturalist Louis Agassiz dismissed the theory as "a scientific mistake, untrue in its facts, unscientific in its method, and mischievous in its tendency." Religious men accused Darwin of blaspheming against God, of destroying the foundations of religion, and even of degrading the human race.

The controversy over evolution raged in learned journals, burst out at scientific meetings, and convulsed the drawing rooms of polite society. Behind the scenes, respected men plotted ways to destroy Darwin's theory, and learned authors, writing under the cloak of anonymity, spitefully misrepresented his ideas. For a long, tense period it seemed that the theory might be overwhelmed by the hatred that it inspired in so many quarters. But Darwin had on his side the force of truth and a few bold allies willing to stand up in defense of that truth. When at last the tide of abuse receded, the theory of evolution stood like an impregnable fortress. Today it still holds its place as one of the greatest discoveries of modern science.

All this was the achievement of a gentle, modest man who somehow had managed to look at the whole world of living things in a new and different way.

Charles Darwin was born in the country town of Shrewsbury, close to the border between England and Wales, on February 12, 1809, the same day that Abraham Lincoln was born in faraway Kentucky. Except for a hatred of slavery, the two men had little in common, however, either in their lives or in the backgrounds from which they sprang. There was nothing of the frontier about the busy market town of Shrewsbury, clustered on hills overlooking the River Severn, or about the rich farmlands of the surrounding county of Shropshire. No cloud of poverty hung over Darwin's childhood; the house he grew up in was large and comfortable, with fine gardens and a superb view of the river, and it was well supplied with servants to do all the household chores.

There was no want of books and learning in Darwin's family background. By birth he belonged to the cultured middle class of England, which was just then rising to prominence and political power. His father, Dr. Robert

Graceful arches of stone bridges span the Severn in this 1825 engraving of Shrewsbury. The river long served as the border between England and Wales; its two ancient bridges are still named for the formerly independent nations.

Darwin, was the leading physician of Shrewsbury and a man widely respected for his shrewd and sympathetic understanding of human nature. This gift had gained for Dr. Darwin a wide practice in the county and considerable personal wealth. With his sharp wit and self-assured manner, Dr. Darwin was an imposing man. He was also an enormous one, since he stood six feet two inches tall and weighed well over three hundred thirty pounds. Charles was deeply in awe of him.

In addition to an impressively successful father, Charles had a most unusual grandfather, who had been offered—and had refused—the post of Royal Physician to King George III. This grandfather, Erasmus Darwin, was renowned not only as a doctor but also as an eccentric amateur philosopher who had written several widely read books about nature. In one of them he had put forward an extraor-

13

dinary idea. All the different kinds of living things, said Erasmus Darwin, had been produced over a period of millions of years from one original ancient parent, each of whose countless offspring had a natural impulse toward "improvement." For saying this the doctor had been accused of atheism, since his idea contradicted what scientists and nonscientists alike took for granted: that God had separately created each and every species of living thing.

It took courage to proclaim such an idea, but Erasmus Darwin was fearlessly independent—a trait common to all the Darwins. They were people who thought their own thoughts and did things in their own quiet, eccentric way. One typical member of the family was Charles' uncle, Erasmus Darwin's second son, who had a passion for collecting statistics. As a boy he set out to make a personal census of his home town by counting the number of houses and guessing how many people lived inside. The official census showed that the boy had made an accurate count.

Charles' mother, Susannah, was a daughter of Erasmus Darwin's great friend Josiah Wedgwood, who had grown rich and renowned throughout Europe as a maker of fine pottery. The Wedgwoods were a talented and unusual family, deeply devoted to philanthropic causes and to the promotion of education and learning. They were freethinkers, and like the Darwins, they refused to be the slaves of respectable opinion. Charles thus grew up in a far more liberal atmosphere than did most middle-class boys of his day.

The Wedgwood influence, however, came mainly from Charles' Wedgwood uncles and cousins, for his mother died when he was eight and a half. For some reason he remembered almost nothing about her. This was odd, he once remarked, because even his younger sister, Catherine (he had four sisters and a brother), remembered her quite well. His only memories of his mother, he said, were "her death-bed, her black velvet gown, and her curiously constructed worktable." The truth was that Charles, both as a boy and as a man, was not a close observer of people, although he was a marvelously sharp observer of physical things. Even as a grown man he could still remember vividly the "shady green road" where, as a child, he had spied a snake and the "wild and irregular course" the sea gulls took along the beach at night one summer by the Welsh seashore.

As a little boy Charles loved to wander about, examining objects. "I tried to make out the names of plants, and collected all sorts of things, shells, seals, franks [mailing marks made on letters before stamps were invented], coins,

Two old friends depicted in Wedgwood medallions: Josiah Wedgwood (far right) and Erasmus Darwin. The founder of the pottery firm also appears below (far right) in a rural setting with his wife and seven children, including eldest daughter, Susannah (at center, on horseback). George Stubbs, renowned as a painter of horses, gave this charming 1780 family portrait a strong equestrian flavor.

Another 1825 view of Shrewsbury shows a gabled, Tudor-style house dating from the sixteenth-century reign of Elizabeth I. Founded in the fifth century, the town stands on the site of a Roman outpost.

and minerals." He also collected birds' eggs, but out of obedience to his sisters, who were very tenderhearted, he took only one egg from each nest. A dislike of cruelty ran very strong in the Darwin family. Dr. Robert Darwin actually hated the sight of blood, and in later years Charles recalled that, when he himself was ten, he asked his sisters whether it was all right to kill insects in order to collect them. They said No.

Even Charles' boyish pranks were concerned with natural objects. At the day school in Shrewsbury that he attended until he was nine, a school friend recalled that Charles came to class one day and announced that he could learn the name of any flower by looking inside the petals. Charles' friend was eager to learn how to do this but Charles would not tell, because, in fact, he had made the whole thing up. He told another school friend that he could turn primroses any color he wished by watering them with certain colored fluids, "which was of course a monstrous fable, and had never been tried by me."

Charles often invented such falsehoods, he recalled many years later, but always "for the sake of causing excitement." Characteristically, his idea of excitement usually concerned the phenomena of nature. Whenever Charles returned from a walk—and he loved to take long, solitary walks—he would invariably claim to have seen "a pheasant or some strange bird." Whether the family was impressed by reports of strange birds is not known. Charles, however, obviously believed that strange birds would be exciting to everybody.

At the age of nine he was enrolled in Shrewsbury School, barely a mile from his home. Dr. Samuel Butler, a noted classical scholar, was the headmaster, and his students were taught Latin, classics, and ancient history, standard grammar-school subjects that Charles found both useless and dull. The students were constantly called on to compose verses in Latin and Greek, and like most of his contemporaries, Charles spent endless hours learning each day's lessons by heart. He would greatly have preferred scientific studies, but in those days science did not form part of any school curriculum. In fact, Dr. Butler, like many other headmasters of the time, cordially disliked science, as Charles discovered one day to his sorrow. His older brother, Erasmus, had built a chemistry laboratory in the family tool house, and Charles used to help him with his experiments. Engaging in such odd and mysterious pursuits led to Charles being nicknamed Gas by his schoolmates, but Dr. Butler was not amused. One day, in front of the entire school, he publicly ridiculed Charles for wasting his time on such a useless subject. Presumably Dr. Butler felt that a student who did so poorly at school ought not to be wasting his time on such out-of-the-way topics as chemistry.

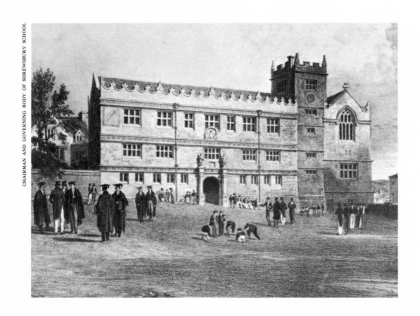

Students and teachers in cap and gown take a break from studies in front of Shrewsbury's Old School. In one of its deep-set windows Darwin loved to sit and read.

Holding a potted plant indicative of his future great interest in botany, six-year-old Charles Darwin posed with his younger sister, Catherine, for the 1816 chalk drawing in color at right. The two were the youngest of six children. In the scene below, by the famous English caricaturist Thomas Rowlandson, a schoolboy begs his master to spare the rod (at left) in punishing him. Darwin was an indifferent student in schools like this, noted for their harsh discipline.

COMBE, *Dance of Life*, 1817: NEW YORK PUBLIC LIBRARY

Certainly Charles was a poor student, since he cared little for his studies and forgot all he learned as soon as he could. "The school as a means of education to me was simply a blank," he once wrote. "I learned absolutely nothing except by amusing myself reading and experimenting in chemistry." On the other hand, he was not one of those noticeably bright children who just happen to do poorly in class. He was not even noticeably bright. He seemed to be just another simple boy who preferred outdoor play to his schoolbooks. As he himself put it, "I was considered by all my masters and by my father as a very ordinary boy, rather below the common standard of intellect."

Being a modest and unassuming boy, Charles thought his elders more or less right in their judgment. He had no burning desire to prove that they were wrong, as he did not take himself very seriously. This is a very important fact about Darwin's youth. It was years before he realized that he was capable of accomplishing something significant in life. As a result, his choice of science as a profession came about more or less indirectly, indeed, partly by accident.

At school, meanwhile, he continued quite contentedly to romp with his beloved dogs, pursue his various hobbies, and above all, go out shooting. By the time he had reached the age of fifteen, shooting game birds had become the ruling passion of his life. "I do not believe," he once said, "that anyone could have shown more zeal for the most holy cause than I did for shooting birds." This zeal reached its peak during his undergraduate days when he spent the falls at Maer, the gracious Elizabethan house belonging to his uncle Josiah Wedgwood, which was situated on a great wooded estate twenty miles from Shrewsbury. At Maer Charles was so eager to shoot, he recalled, "that I used to place my shooting boots open by my bed-side when I went to bed, so as not to lose half-a-minute in putting them on in the morning."

In shooting, as in everything else he later did, Charles approached matters earnestly and methodically. He spent hours practicing before a mirror the proper method of throwing his gun up to his shoulder. Out shooting, he used to carry in his buttonhole a string in which he tied a knot whenever he downed a bird. The sight of Charles tallying his score as carefully as a bookkeeper prompted some of his friends to play a joke on him. Out shooting one day, Charles found that every time he shot a bird and was about to record the score, he would see one or another of his friends reloading his gun. "You must not count that bird," they

Darwin's schoolboy scribbling has been preserved in his atlas flyleaf. Later he would bitterly resent his inability to draw even the simplest sketches of scientific specimens.

would say, "for I fired at the same time." The gamekeeper, who was in on the jest, would nod his head in agreement. This happened time after time, but it took Charles the whole day to catch on. He was a very gullible young man.

In the upper-middle-class world of the early nineteenth century, only younger sons without money or prospects expected to have to work for a living. Working meant entering one of the gentlemanly professions, such as law, medicine, or the Army or Navy. (No man who considered himself a gentleman ever became a businessman, or to use the expression then current, "went into trade.") As a result, there was no sense of its being wrong, or even surprising, for a young man to expect to live entirely on an allowance from his father or an income inherited after his death. Indeed, it was perfectly possible for a country gentleman to spend his

Partridge shooting, as depicted in this 1820 aquatint by Thomas Sutherland, was a gentleman's sport. Sleek, well-trained dogs flush out the birds (far right)

whole life in riding, shooting, and pursuing the various hobbies that interested him—provided he had inherited enough money to support his family as well as himself.

Dr. Darwin, however, looked with dismay on his son's idle ways. "You care for nothing but shooting, dogs, and rat-catching," he told Charles one day, "and you will be a disgrace to yourself and all your family." Accordingly, he decided to take Charles out of Dr. Butler's school and send him to study medicine at Edinburgh University. Charles was only sixteen, but his brother, Erasmus, was already studying medicine at Edinburgh and Dr. Darwin wanted Charles to begin a career before he could waste any more time. So in October, 1825, Charles went to Scotland.

He had not been at Edinburgh three months when he wrote his sister that one of his medical courses "cannot be

SCHWERDT, *Hunting, Hawking, Shooting*, 1928: NEW YORK PUBLIC LIBRARY

for the hunters, elegantly dressed in frock coats and top hats. In a field next to the imposing manor house (center, background), harvesting is under way.

While out shooting in open fields, hunters and servants communicated with each other by means of formal signals. Above, left to right, are recognized signs for: Have you marked any birds? Bring the powder and shot; Dog wanted; and— surely welcome news—luncheon.

translated into any word expressive of its stupidity." Sitting in lecture halls on cold winter mornings to hear dull professors droning on about drugs he found as painfully tedious as Dr. Butler's curriculum had been. Like many other freshman medical students, he shuddered at the thought of dissecting a human cadaver, and when he had to watch a child being operated on—this was in the days before anesthesia— the sight was so ghastly that he fled the operating room.

Such squeamishness must be overcome by anyone who wishes to be a doctor, but Charles really had no intention of ever practicing medicine. Not long after coming to Edinburgh, he had learned that he would inherit enough money from his father to be able to live in comfort without having to work for a living. This news, he admitted, "was sufficient to check any strenuous effort to learn medicine." He regularly attended meetings of the Edinburgh scientific societies, however, and after hearing the great American naturalist John James Audubon lecturing on North American birds, young Darwin took lessons in the art of stuffing birds from a Negro taxidermist. He also made friends with the oyster fishermen at the nearby port of Newhaven, who taught him how to cast fishing nets. He tried to dissect the specimens he obtained but confessed later that "from not having had any regular practice in dissection, and from possessing only a wretched microscope, my attempts were very poor."

After two years of futile studies at medical school Charles was finally reprieved by Dr. Darwin, who realized that his son disliked medicine intensely. He proposed instead that Charles move to Cambridge University and study to become a minister of the Church of England. At that time it was not considered necessary to have any particular religious calling to become a clergyman—it was a profession not unlike others. Charles, however, had some scruples about being able to accept all the Church's religious dogmas, although in many ways he found the plan quite appealing.

A clergyman with a private income could live quite comfortably in a country parish and enjoy considerable leisure for shooting. He could collect birds' eggs and insects to his heart's content. Indeed, it was considered an especially fine thing in those days for a clergyman to study nature, since it was widely believed that the study of living things was a great support of religious faith. Nature was God's creation and the more a man studied it, the more he would learn about the power and wisdom of its Creator. Naturalists enjoyed pointing out how cunningly God had designed the human eye, the feather of a peacock, and even the joint on the antenna of an earwig. By studying such things, a clergyman could demonstrate *scientifically* that God was all-powerful and wise.

After taking some time to decide that he did not doubt "the strict and literal truth of every word in the Bible," Charles took up residence at Cambridge in January, 1828, to study classics, mathematics, and theology.

He was just nineteen, a tall, gray-eyed, friendly young man. Christ's College, Cambridge, where he was enrolled, then had the reputation of being rather "horsey," which meant that it was filled with wealthy young country gentlemen much like Charles himself. Simple, zestful, and "as ignorant as a pig," as he put it, Charles found many friends among the sporting set. These easygoing, lively young men rode horses, went shooting, and studied as little as possible. Darwin and his cronies loved to eat hearty dinners, sing loud songs, and play practical jokes, often on Charles himself, for he was as gullible and hard to offend as ever.

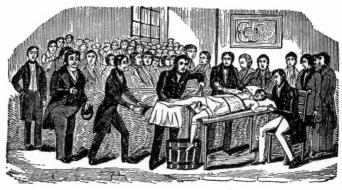

The agony of an amputation without anesthesia is shown in a period engraving (right). Securely strapped to the table, a fifteen-year-old boy submits to the surgeon's knife. Men stronger than Charles Darwin found such gruesome medical practices unbearable.

DENTAL ITEMS OF INTEREST PUBLISHING CO.

Among all these jolly fellows Charles was one of the jolliest. He had scarcely a care in the world, except about spending more than his allowance. He managed to pass his examinations by intensive spells of hard work, which he kept as brief as possible. Everyone who knew Charles liked him. "The most genial, warm-hearted, generous, and affectionate of friends . . . good, and just, and loveable," said a Cambridge friend, recalling young Darwin years later.

Almost all that distinguished Charles from his comrades was his curious passion for collecting beetles, which he would search for incessantly up and down the flat Cambridgeshire water meadows. He made beetle hunting so merry a sport that he even got some of his cronies to help him "entomologize," as he called it. Sometimes, in his letters, Charles would refer to his beetles with mock seriousness as "The Science," but he was not strictly scientific, he confessed. "It was the mere passion for collecting, for I did not dissect them and rarely compared their external characters with published descriptions, but got them named anyhow."

It was a hobby nicely suited to a future country parson, but it meant little more to him. The man who would one day become the greatest of all biologists had not the slightest expectation of making a serious contribution to science. When a college friend remarked casually that Charles

Cambridge University's carefully tended botanic gardens are shown at left in an 1815 engraving. Beyond the greenhouse are the pinnacles of King's College Chapel, where Darwin, a constant visitor, enjoyed listening to choral music.

The early-nineteenth-century ideal of a country parson as a naturalist is satirized in the Rowlandson engraving above. As a gentleman and two admiring ladies look over his shoulder, the thoughtful cleric sketches the barnyard's inhabitants. The crowding animals seem to share the humorous disdain of the old woman (far right).

would be elected some day to a fellowship in the Royal Society, England's most illustrious scientific organization, "the notion," Darwin recalled, "seemed to me preposterous." Dr. Darwin would have agreed. He feared his son was growing into what he disparagingly called "an idle sporting man."

There was, however, one man at Cambridge who saw more in Charles Darwin than either he or his family suspected. Professor John Stevens Henslow had become chairman of the botany department three years before Darwin arrived at Cambridge, and his charm and his enthusiasm for his subject had already promoted an interest in natural history among many of the undergraduates. Charles' beetle collecting and his curiosity about living things made a

25

Cambridge University students of Darwin's day always wore traditional caps and gowns. The scholar poring over his books above is perhaps dreaming—as young Darwin did—of travel beyond the seas.

strong impression on Henslow, who was still only in his early thirties, and the young professor and the young beetle collector became fast friends. Henslow was one of the first adults to take Darwin seriously, but although he urged his pupil to take a more serious interest in science, he made little headway. Charles could not get it out of his mind that natural history, for him, was a hobby. It was not Henslow's belief in his ability but the romance of adventure that was to set off the first spark of ambition in Charles.

In the winter of 1830–31 he began reading a travel book, *A Personal Narrative of Travels to the Equinoctial Regions of America During the Years 1790–1804.* Written by Baron Alexander von Humboldt, the greatest scientific explorer of the age, it described the author's epic journey to the Canary Islands, South America, Mexico, and the United States. These countries, and indeed most of the world, were then almost virgin territory for a naturalist to study, and explorers other than Humboldt were setting out to climb nameless mountains and cross unmapped wastes in order to bring back new species of plants and animals. Darwin had been born into the great age of scientific exploration, and Humboldt's book gave him an intoxicating glimpse of the joys of such work. He was especially thrilled by the baron's description of Tenerife, in the Canary Islands, and began hatching wild schemes to go there and see the wonders of its tropical scenery for himself. He started studying Spanish and wrote to Henslow, who he hoped would come with him, "I hope you fan your Canary ardour. I read and re-read Humboldt; do you do the same?"

In September, 1831, when Darwin was twenty-two, the great opportunity came, quite unexpectedly.

He had graduated from Cambridge creditably, but without honors, in January, 1831, but had to stay some extra months in order to complete his residence requirements for a B.A. degree. He spent much time on long walks with Henslow, who successfully interested him in taking up geology—the study of the earth's history through the examination of its rocky crust. At Henslow's house he met Adam Sedgwick, who had held the chair of geology at Cambridge since 1818. At the time of his election, Sedgwick, a clergyman, knew nothing at all about geology but he had speedily mastered his new subject and become an eminent and respected geologist. In August Darwin had the honor of accompanying him on a brief field trip to North Wales, but as soon as the shooting season approached, he promptly packed up his gear and left Wales in order to reach Maer by September 1. "At that time I would have thought myself mad to give up the first days of partridge shooting for geology or any other science."

Returning home to Shrewsbury on his way to Maer, he found a letter from Henslow awaiting him. It contained electrifying news. A certain Captain Robert Fitzroy of the Royal Navy was sailing around the world on a surveying trip that autumn and he wanted a young naturalist to be his companion without pay aboard H.M.S. *Beagle*. "Don't put on any modest doubts or fears about your disqualifications, for I assure you I think you are the very man they are in search of," wrote Henslow reassuringly.

HUMBOLDT, *Voyage aux Regions Equinoxiales . . .*, 1810–34: NEW YORK PUBLIC LIBRARY

The lure Humboldt's Travels *exerted upon Darwin as an undergraduate is easily sensed from a study of this illustration, based on the German traveler's sketch, of a fruit-laden balsa raft moored on a river in Ecuador.*

A plain-ended hammer whose foot-long haft can be used as a measure is every geologist's most vital tool. This one accompanied Darwin throughout his long voyage.

It was like a dream come true. Then, in one of those heartbreaking reversals of fortune, the beautiful bubble burst. Dr. Darwin refused to give Charles permission to go. He reeled off half-a-dozen crushing reasons why his son should not set sail around the world, including his belief that the voyage would make him unfit for a clergyman's life. The ever-confident doctor was so sure the trip was a folly that he added one tiny loophole that soon changed his son's entire career. "If you can find any man of common sense, who advises you to go," Dr. Darwin declared, "I will give my consent." Poor Charles was sure he could never find such a man, so he wrote Henslow the next day sadly declining the offer. Then, for the first time in his life, he went off to shoot partridges with a heavy heart.

At Maer, however, all the Wedgwoods took quite a different attitude toward the plan. To that enlightened family the offer seemed, as it did to Charles himself, too good to refuse. Encouraged by their support, he sent a messenger to his father with a letter begging him to change his mind. Josiah Wedgwood II, Charles' "Uncle Jos," added a note outlining his reasons for believing the trip was a good idea, since "the pursuit of Natural History, though certainly not professional, is very suitable to a clergyman." The following morning, Uncle Jos and Charles drove to Shrewsbury to intercede with Dr. Darwin personally.

When they arrived, Charles found his father true to his word. In the upright and judicious person of Josiah Wedgwood, Charles had found the "man of common sense" who favored the trip. Dr. Darwin consented to let him go. This was the first time in his life that Charles had bested his father, and he tried to cheer him up a little by pointing out the practical advantages of the voyage. He remarked hopefully that it would be a fine way to save money, since "I should be deuced clever to spend more than my allowance whilst aboard the *Beagle*." With a smile, his father replied, "But they tell me you are very clever."

After traveling to Cambridge to break the news to Henslow, Darwin then hastened to London to face the biggest obstacle of all: the personal interview with Captain Fitzroy, the twenty-six-year-old commander of H.M.S. *Beagle*. The interview was not an entirely pleasant prospect, for the captain was an aristocrat with an iron will and a stern devotion to what he considered his duty. Indeed, one of Fitzroy's reasons for undertaking at least two years of rigorous survey work aboard the *Beagle* was that on his previous voyage he had brought back three primitive tribes-

Josiah Wedgwood II

men from southernmost South America. He had paid for their support and Christian education while they were in England, and he now wished to bring them home again, to spread Christianity among their countrymen. A deeply religious man, Fitzroy had his own private reason for wanting a naturalist aboard the *Beagle*. He was convinced that he would find scientific proof that the Book of Genesis was literally true. Little did he know what his naturalist would discover instead.

Immediately Darwin met him, Fitzroy bluntly described the grim prospects ahead: the voyage would be rough, the work hard, and the food plain. Would Darwin be prepared to bear up cheerfully under such privations? Charles said he would. "Shall you bear being told that I want the cabin to myself—when I want to be alone?" Charles said he could. When the interview ended, he was convinced that he had made a favorable impression. Actually, by one of those curious strokes of fate, he had not. While Charles was listening intently to the captain, the captain was looking intently at Darwin's nose. Fitzroy placed great stock in the "science" of physiognomy, which supposedly tells what a man is like by a proper examination of his facial features. Alas for Darwin, he had inherited his father's broad snub nose, which, according to physiognomy, indicates a man lacking in character. This was a serious mark against him in the captain's opinion.

For several days Charles suffered a fever of anxiety while the captain pondered the matter. Finally, however, after another meeting with Darwin, Fitzroy decided that he was an admirable young man, snub nose or no snub nose. Charles' happy temperament had triumphed over physiognomy and the last hurdle was leaped. All Darwin had to do now was to collect the equipment he would need for the long voyage and then wait nervously in port as one delay after another kept the ship from sailing. "My chief employment is to go on board the *Beagle*," he wrote Henslow on November 15, "and try to look as much like a sailor as I can. I have no evidence of having taken in man, woman, or child."

Whether he looked like a sailor or not, Charles did not have much longer to wait. On December 27, 1831, the *Beagle* hoisted anchor and set out to sea, not to return for five long years. Darwin's voyage aboard the *Beagle*, "by far the greatest event of my life," was about to commence. When it was over, neither Darwin nor science would ever again be quite the same.

"She is the admiration of the whole place," Darwin boasted of the **Beagle**, *seen at right in this water color.*

II

OUTWARD BOUND ON H.M.S. BEAGLE

To circumnavigate the globe on a ninety-foot sailing ship is a gallant undertaking, especially for a man who has never been to sea in his life. But Charles Darwin did not feel very gallant during the first two weeks of his voyage. As the little vessel pitched and rolled through mountainous waves off the coast of France, the *Beagle*'s twenty-two-year-old naturalist lay seasick in his cabin, wondering why he had ever set foot on board. He was earning his sea legs the hard way, for he bunked with the expedition's surveyor in the part of the ship that pitched the most: the poop cabin in the stern. This tiny cabin was all but filled by the *Beagle*'s chart table, at one end of which was Darwin's office and laboratory. Also on that side of the cabin were tiers of drawers that held his clothes and scientific equipment. His bed was a hammock strung above the charts, and he could lie full length only by removing a top drawer and sticking his feet into the empty space. "I have just enough room to turn around," he wrote to Henslow, "and that is all."

While Darwin lay in his hammock surviving on raisins, the three-masted brig beat its way south into tropical waters. Its destination was the Atlantic coast of South America. Eventually the *Beagle* would round Cape Horn and head across the Pacific Ocean, but that day lay far in the future. Captain Fitzroy's primary mission was to make a detailed survey of South America's southern coasts for the British Admiralty, and it was a laborious task. Although assigned to peaceful duties, the *Beagle* was a Royal Navy ship of war, mounting six guns and maintaining strict naval discipline. Darwin's first experience of this came even before the *Beagle* put to sea. Several of the men celebrated Christmas, 1831, by getting very drunk, and the next day was spent in administering the standard punishment for such misconduct—brutal floggings with the cat-o'-nine-tails.

Thanks to the foresight of Captain Fitzroy, the Beagle *voyage was well illustrated. Augustus Earle, the expedition's draftsman, sketched the spirited shenanigans of crossing the equator on February 7, 1832 (top). In the traditional initiation, seamen, including Darwin, crossing the line for the first time are led blindfolded to "Neptune," then tarred and dunked in water. At Montevideo, Conrad Martens replaced the ailing Earle as ship's artist. He depicted the* Beagle *beached in 1834 for repairs to her keel and a new copper sheathing (above) and Fuegians in canoes welcoming the vessel to a glacial fiord at the tip of South America (right). Midshipman Philip Gidley King drew the side elevation (opposite, top), showing Fitzroy's cabin (1) and Darwin's seat at the chart table in the poop cabin (2, including the drawers at 3 into which his feet went).*

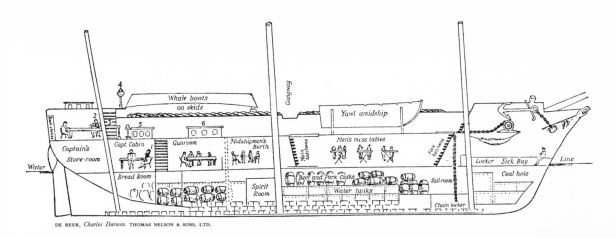

Whale boats on skids

Gangway

Yawl amidship

4

Captain's Store-room

2

5

Capt. Cabin

Gunroom

6

Midshipmen's Berth

Men's mess tables

Water

Bread Room

Spirit Room

Beef and Pork Casks

Water tanks

Sail room

Fore hatchway

Locker Sick Bay

Coal hole

Line

Chain locker

DE BEER, *Charles Darwin*. THOMAS NELSON & SONS, LTD.

Robert Fitzroy, captain of the Beagle, *was portrayed as Vice-Admiral—an appointment he received some time after the return from his voyage with Darwin.*

The sight sickened Darwin as thoroughly as the operations without anesthesia that he had been forced to watch in Edinburgh. But he had much faith in Captain Fitzroy and continued to admire him. He feared him a little, too, for the captain was moody and apt to fly into terrible rages, especially in the early mornings. When Fitzroy lost his temper, Darwin found him completely unreasonable, and nothing made the captain angrier than hearing unorthodox opinions on matters of politics and religion. Young as he was, Fitzroy hated new ideas. Fortunately, he liked Darwin and soon reported to the Admiralty that his naturalist-companion was "a regular Trump." It never occurred to Fitzroy that his mild-mannered shipmate would come to harbor unorthodox scientific ideas.

It never occurred to Darwin either. As a naturalist, he saw himself simply as a humble collector of specimens. As he wrote Professor Henslow, he was mainly worried about whether he would bring back the right specimens, for he was well aware that he had very little formal scientific training. Yet this, although Darwin did not know it, was one of his greatest assets. Had he been trained as a professional scientist, he might have thought like one. And in 1831 the accepted theories of professional naturalists were not only highly convincing; they were totally misleading.

To a naturalist of that time the world's population of plants and animals was divided into distinctive groups known as species. The lion, the flounder, the English sparrow, and the oak tree were—and are—common examples of the more than a million living species. Nearly all naturalists of the 1830's believed that each species had been specially and individually created by God, and the most fundamental fact about them was that they never changed, despite the passing of time. For as long as man had kept records, each species had remained the same. Lions gave birth to lions and only to lions, flounders spawned nothing but flounders, oak trees produced oak trees. Children resembled their parents, and therefore members of a species could only produce offspring that closely resembled themselves. Thus each species remained fixed and unchanging for generation after generation. In addition, since no new species ever appeared by itself, scientists had every reason to believe that no new species ever *would* appear, except by an act of God.

New discoveries in the science of geology seemed to give added support to the fundamental doctrine that species never changed. Examining the earth's strata, geologists had found that these layers of rock could be recognized and classified on the basis of their age by the fossil remains that they contained.

Fossils are the impressions left in solid rock of creatures and plants that had been alive when that particular rock layer formed the surface of the earth. In the lowest, most ancient rocks, geologists found no signs of life at all. In the strata just above were fossils of small, lowly, sea-going creatures unlike any that currently existed. They called these layers Primary strata, and the highest types of life found in them were fishes and primitive, land-dwelling reptiles.

In the layers lying directly above the Primary strata, however, an interesting development had taken place. Apparently, all the lowly creatures of the Primary strata had utterly disappeared. In these new layers, which geologists called Secondary strata, a wholly different set of creatures had taken their place. Even the fishes of this period were quite unlike the fish species of the earlier time, while the fossilized remains of reptiles showed that this particular animal form had reached its climax in spectacular monsters, which were given the name dinosaurs.

Above the Secondary rocks geologists found a thick series of strata that they called Tertiary, or third, strata. The fossils in these layers appeared to show that all the earlier forms of life had come to an abrupt end too and had been replaced by fresh species. These included creatures more advanced than reptiles: warm-blooded animals known as mammals that gave birth, not to eggs, but to living young. In the most recent rocks, which were christened Quaternary, or fourth, strata, the kinds of species again changed. New forms of plants and animals appeared, familiar forms, almost identical with modern species.*

In nearly all these rock layers, fossil remains were found in quantity, and classification of them into time periods revealed—or seemed to reveal—a striking fact: each species appeared and disappeared *suddenly*.

---

*As geologists made further researches into the earth's history, they found it more convenient to classify the various rock layers according to time. The Primary strata were assigned to the Paleozoic era (a word meaning "ancient"), and this was subdivided into six periods of time, each named for a different system of rock strata. The Secondary rocks became part of the Mesozoic (middle) era, subdivided into three periods, while the terms Tertiary and Quaternary themselves became the names of periods within the Cenozoic, or relatively recent, era. To make these periods easier to visualize, geological tables showed the stages of the earth's development like the layers of a cake, with the Paleozoic rocks at the bottom and the most recent at the top.

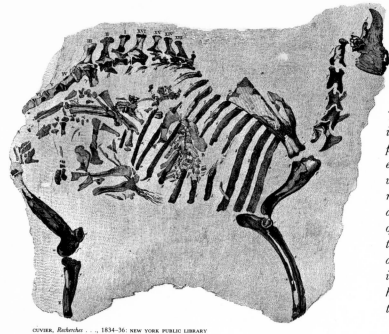

The Paleotherium Minus *fossil at left illustrated the 1834–36 edition of Cuvier's pioneering study of fossil bones. The skeleton of this ancestor of the tapir was unearthed, almost complete, embedded in rocks more than 21 million years old, in a village near Paris. The 1888 "Table of Stratified Rocks" at right classifies the geological strata in time sequence, along with typical fossils that are found in each period. Although recent research has brought further subdivisions, the system has remained basically unchanged.*

William "Strata" Smith

Georges Cuvier

THE GEOLOGICAL RECORD

Toward the end of the eighteenth century, scientists had begun trying to analyze the various layers of rocks that make up the earth's surface and to identify the fossils that were so often found in them. Since the study of geology was available to anyone who cared to take a hammer and chip away at the rocks in the surrounding countryside, this new science attracted many enthusiastic and knowledgeable amateurs. One of these was William Smith, a surveyor who toured England in the 1790's to map out suitable routes for the canal network that linked the country's industrial centers. He was the first man to realize that the types of fossils found in each rock layer differ markedly from those in other strata and that the lowest layer of rock must obviously be the most ancient. "Strata Smith," as he was nicknamed, had discovered a fundamental geological fact: part of the earth's history could be read in the record of the fossils left behind by each bygone age.

In Darwin's day the basic concepts in this new science of geology were just beginning to be filled in, in detail, by a younger generation of geologists. They relied mainly upon the work of a brilliant French anatomist, Georges Cuvier. His study of fossil bones, shells, and other relics of ancient creatures proved to his own satisfaction, and that of a large group of followers, that species could not have changed of themselves but must have been created anew, and in improved forms, after a series of catastrophic upheavals had devastated the surface of the earth.

TABLE OF STRATIFIED ROCKS.

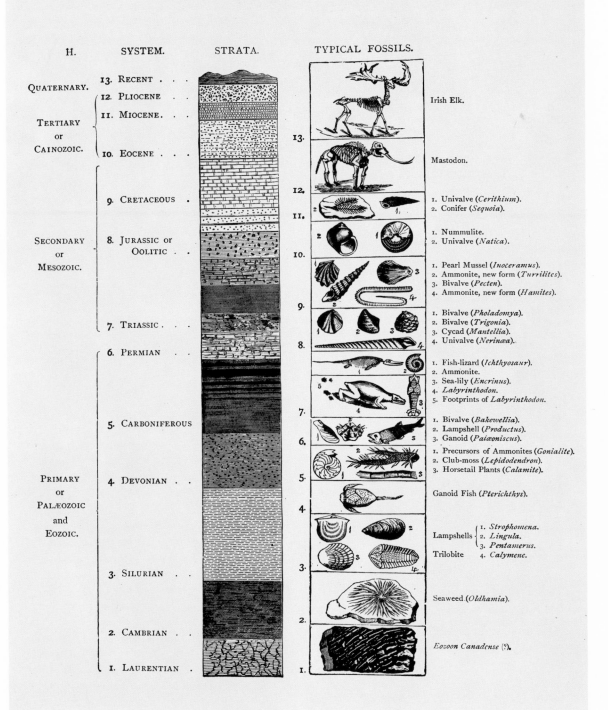

H.	SYSTEM.	STRATA.	TYPICAL FOSSILS.
QUATERNARY.	13. RECENT . . .		
TERTIARY or CAINOZOIC.	12. PLIOCENE . .		13. Irish Elk.
	11. MIOCENE. .		
	10. EOCENE . . .		12. Mastodon.
SECONDARY or MESOZOIC.	9. CRETACEOUS .		11. 1. Univalve (*Cerithium*). 2. Conifer (*Sequoia*).
	8. JURASSIC or OOLITIC . .		10. 1. Nummulite. 2. Univalve (*Natica*).
			9. 1. Pearl Mussel (*Inoceramus*). 2. Ammonite, new form (*Turrilites*). 3. Bivalve (*Pecten*). 4. Ammonite, new form (*Hamites*).
	7. TRIASSIC . . .		8. 1. Bivalve (*Pholadomya*). 2. Bivalve (*Trigonia*). 3. Cycad (*Mantellia*). 4. Univalve (*Nerinæa*).
	6. PERMIAN . .		7. 1. Fish-lizard (*Ichthyosaur*). 2. Ammonite. 3. Sea-lily (*Encrinus*). 4. *Labyrinthodon*. 5. Footprints of *Labyrinthodon*.
PRIMARY or PALÆOZOIC and EOZOIC.	5. CARBONIFEROUS		6. 1. Bivalve (*Bakewellia*). 2. Lampshell (*Productus*). 3. Ganoid (*Palæoniscus*).
			5. 1. Precursors of Ammonites (*Gonialite*). 2. Club-moss (*Lepidodendron*). 3. Horsetail Plants (*Calamite*).
	4. DEVONIAN . .		4. Ganoid Fish (*Pterichthys*).
	3. SILURIAN . .		3. Lampshells { 1. *Strophomena*. 2. *Lingula*. 3. *Pentamerus*. } Trilobite 4. *Calymene*.
	2. CAMBRIAN . .		2. Seaweed (*Oldhamia*).
	1. LAURENTIAN .		1. *Eozoon Canadense* (?).

37

This extinction of primitive species and the sudden appearance of new, more advanced species were taken by many scientists as positive proof that every species must have been individually created by God. After all, they argued, in what other way could a new kind of living thing come suddenly into existence? Darwin's grandfather Erasmus had speculated that all creatures might have developed from one original parent, but the fossil record seemed to disprove this completely.

The most widely accepted view among geologists was that God had created the world as we know it in several separate stages. At different times during the earth's long history His creative force had unleashed great storms and floods, titanic catastrophes that altered the shape of oceans and continents and crumpled mountains and valleys into relief. At the same time, each catastrophe destroyed all the living things that God had previously created—which explained the sudden disappearance of the ancient species. In their place the creative force produced a whole new set of species—which accounted for the sudden appearance of fresh species in the fossil record. As each catastrophe occurred and was followed by a fresh creation of higher forms of life, the earth and its species gradually took on more familiar shapes. Finally, after the last great cataclysm, which was thought to have occurred at the end of the Tertiary period, the plants and animals of our modern era were created, and man appeared on earth for the first time.

This theory, understandably, was known as "catastrophism." Like any widely accepted theory, it fitted most of the facts and answered the chief questions that scientists were asking. That it did not answer all of them, however, had just been brilliantly proved by an able young lawyer turned geologist, named Charles Lyell. In 1830 he published the first volume of *The Principles of Geology*, in which he argued that the history of the earth had always been governed by the same agents of wind, water, and fire that were familiar in the present. It was not necessary for each period of development to be ended by a sudden supernatural catastrophe, Lyell said. Provided that a sufficiently long amount of time had elapsed, the same effects could have been produced by natural forces, such as erosion by sea, wind, and rain, and upheavals caused by volcanic activity within the earth.

Lyell was not a lawyer for nothing. He phrased his theory carefully and argued his case with such clarity and conviction that his book at once created quite a stir in Eng-

Charles Lyell (above) began issuing his three-volume Principles of Geology *in 1830. Its controversial ideas aroused such interest that by 1835, as the title page below shows, the expanded work was already in its fourth edition.*

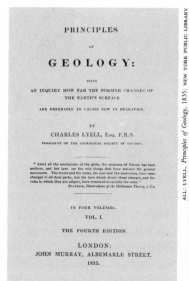

PRINCIPLES

OF

GEOLOGY:

BEING

AN INQUIRY HOW FAR THE FORMER CHANGES OF
THE EARTH'S SURFACE

ARE REFERABLE TO CAUSES NOW IN OPERATION.

BY

CHARLES LYELL, Esq. F.R.S.
PRESIDENT OF THE GEOLOGICAL SOCIETY OF LONDON.

"Amid all the revolutions of the globe, the economy of Nature has been uniform, and her laws are the only things that have resisted the general movement. The rivers and the rocks, the seas and the continents, have been changed in all their parts; but the laws which direct those changes, and the rules to which they are subject, have remained invariably the same."
PLAYFAIR, *Illustrations of the Huttonian Theory*, § 374.

IN FOUR VOLUMES.
VOL. I.

THE FOURTH EDITION.

LONDON:
JOHN MURRAY, ALBEMARLE STREET.
1835.

lish scientific circles. Even Henslow, himself a firm believer in catastrophism, had urged Darwin to take a copy of Lyell's first volume with him on his voyage, because it was so interesting. "But," he cautioned, "do not pay any attention to it except in regard to facts, for it is altogether wild as far as theory goes." En route south, the seasick naturalist read Lyell's "wild" book with eager interest.

On January 6, 1832, the great peak of Tenerife, in the Canary Islands, "was seen amongst the clouds like another world," and Darwin prepared to spend a week realizing his dreams by following in the footsteps of Baron von Humboldt, while enjoying fresh fruit and beautiful views. His hopes were dashed at once: a severe cholera epidemic had been raging when the *Beagle* left England, and the Tenerife authorities would not let the ship's crew land.

It was not until January 16 that Darwin finally had a chance to set his wobbly legs on solid ground. That day the *Beagle* put into the volcanic island of São Tiago in the Cape Verdes, an archipelago some fifteen hundred miles northeast of South America. Captain Fitzroy declared the island to be an extremely dull place, "though interesting enough to a geologist," he added, knowing that Darwin had a different opinion. To Darwin, São Tiago was fascinating— "if, indeed, a person, fresh from sea, and who has just walked, for the first time, in a grove of cocoanut trees, can be a judge of anything but his own happiness." He was at last under a tropical sky, where almost every living creature was new to him. As he wrote joyfully in his diary, he was

Lyell's thesis that natural forces had always shaped the earth was illustrated by the engulfing of Reculver Church, in Kent. Constant erosion brought the sea from a mile away in the 1530's to within eighty yards in 1781 (above) and to its doorstep in 1834 (right).

"hearing the notes of unknown birds, & seeing new insects fluttering about still newer flowers."

Darwin quickly started to "naturalize" on the island. With his plain face red from the sun and his pockets bulging with geological hammer, compass, knife, collecting bags, and field notebook, he explored São Tiago on horseback. Hungrily he observed everything in sight. He examined the island's volcanic rocks and noted how the trade winds permanently bent the island's trees. Darwin had no theory in mind, he just had an insatiable appetite for facts. With intense concentration he watched the antics of a cuttlefish trapped on the beach after the tide ran out. Several times the frightened cuttlefish sprayed a jet of water into the face peering down at it. This behavior Darwin carefully noted down in his journal. "It appeared to me," he wrote, "that it could certainly take good aim." This was not a useless observation. He was already storing up knowledge of how living things protect themselves and thus manage to survive.

On April 4, the *Beagle*, having crossed the Atlantic, set Darwin ashore in Rio de Janeiro for another extended stay on land. He spent three months at the Brazilian capital, happily collecting tropical insects and unhappily observing man-made misery that all but ruined his pleasure in the beautiful tropical scenery.

Brazil in those days was a slaveholding country, and Darwin hated slavery from the bottom of his heart. He half hoped, he wrote his sister, that the slaves would revolt. "It is impossible," he told her, "to see a negro and not feel kindly towards him." Yet he once had to watch while his host beat a six-year-old slave boy with a whip for bringing Darwin a glass of cloudy water. Wherever he turned in Brazil, the ugly evidence of slavery surrounded him. Riding on a ferryboat one day, he tried to communicate with a slave by waving his hands in sign language. The slave, thinking Darwin was going to hit him, dropped his hands to await the blow. "I shall never forget my feelings of surprise, disgust, and shame," wrote Darwin, "at seeing a great powerful man afraid even to ward off a blow."

It was fortunate for Darwin, therefore, that the *Beagle*'s chief surveying duties lay not in Brazil but in Argentina, along a line of coast that stretched twelve hundred miles from the River Plate, to Tierra del Fuego, an island at the storm-swept southern tip of the entire New World.

Argentina was to be Darwin's "home" for the next two years. In many ways it resembled the frontier country of the United States, although life there was even more violent

The treatment of slaves in Brazil appalled Darwin, who detested a system that permitted such brutalities as this beating of a bound slave by his plantation overseer.

FITZROY, *Narrative of the . . . Beagle,* 1839: NEW YORK PUBLIC LIBRARY

and lawless than in the American West at its wildest. Along with the other nations of South America, Argentina had only recently won its independence, and the country was in a state of constant political upheaval. The power of the central government was feeble, and the more remote provinces were dominated by rugged cattle barons. These men owned vast ranches (called *estancias*) on the rolling Argentine Pampas, or grasslands, and ruled them like private kingdoms. Their cowboys were known as Gauchos, and as Darwin remarked, "a more throat-cutting gentry never existed." Farther south, the cattle ranches were fewer, and the Pampas were ruled by warlike, horse-riding Indians, whose reputation for fierceness rivaled even that of the Sioux and Apaches in the United States. To control them, soldiers were stationed in lonely forts on permanent duty as Indian fighters. It was a turbulent region.

"All South America is in such an unsettled state that we have not entered one port without some sort of disturb-

Augustus Earle recorded this harborside scene at Rio de Janeiro, the Beagle's *first major port of call. As slaves carry loads along the dock, a boatload of sailors pulls ashore (right) to sample the delights of Brazil's capital city.*

41

ance," Darwin reported to a friend. "At Buenos Ayres a shot came whistling over our heads; it is a noise I had never before heard, but I found I had an instinctive knowledge of what it meant."

A harbor boat had fired a warning shot across the *Beagle*'s bow, but all it accomplished was to make Captain Fitzroy angry. The *Beagle*'s guns came out in a moment as the Captain ordered his ship to pull up beside the offending vessel. "If your ship bothers us again," he shouted across the narrow span of water, "we will send a whole broadside into her rotten hulk."

The Argentine boat troubled them no further, but there was no peace on the River Plate. When the *Beagle* arrived in Montevideo, Uruguay, just across the river from Buenos Aires, the Army was in a state of mutiny. The mutiny threatened to topple the government, which had itself just overthrown the legal government of the newly independent state. Revolutions, Darwin observed, were occurring almost once a month in this part of the world.

Conditions were almost as uncertain in the other ports the Englishmen visited, as the *Beagle* sailed slowly south along the coast. On September 7 the crew landed at a distant frontier settlement known as Bahía Blanca, a tiny outpost huddled in the heart of Indian country, three hundred miles south of Buenos Aires. In its four-year history it had already been attacked many times by fierce Araucanian Indians. Its fort was a wild-looking place, surrounded by thick mud walls. Inside were nearly naked Indian prisoners and soldiers wearing such ragged clothes that they looked like a gang of bandits. But of all the fort's rough inhabitants, the most striking were the Gauchos, whom Darwin now met for the first time. Each of these swarthy, swaggering cowboys, he noted, wore a brightly colored shawl wrapped tightly around his waist, with a sinister dagger tucked inside, and high, rawhide boots adorned with jangling spurs several inches in diameter. Many also sported vicious-looking knife scars across their faces. "In fighting," Darwin noted, "each party tries to mark the face of his adversary by slashing his nose or eye." Cutthroats though the Gauchos often were, Darwin was to spend many a day on the desolate plains escorted by no one but a few loyal Gaucho companions.

If the sight of the Bahía Blanca fort startled the *Beagle*'s crew, they themselves looked as strange to the people of that lonely and rarely visited outpost. The fort's commander was convinced that the *Beagle*'s landing party was reconnoi-

An Argentinian Gaucho, or cowboy, in colorful dress and heavy spurs, carries a bola—the weighted cord with which he can bring down cows, ostriches, or even, if need be, men. The Gauchos were excessively polite, Darwin noted, but "they seem quite as ready, if occasion offered, to cut your throat."

tering for an attack and had the entire group brought to the fort for cross-examination. Darwin was the first to be questioned by an old major, who seemed to be the garrison's most experienced officer.

Neither the major nor anyone else at the fort had ever heard of such a creature as *un naturalista*. When the major asked in puzzlement what that was, the interpreter replied that a naturalist was "a man who knows everything." At that, the old soldier grew really alarmed. The English visitors were returned to their ship with an escort of armed Gauchos watching their every move.

It was at Bahía Blanca, however, that Darwin took his first notable step toward the theory of evolution. Some twenty-five miles beyond the fort he came upon a gravelly beach known as Punta Alta. There, on September 23, 1832, he wrote in his diary, "to my great joy, I found the head of some large animal stuck in a soft rock. It took me nearly three hours to get it out. As far as I am able to judge, it is allied to the Rhinocerous." Returning to Punta Alta some days later, he found an even more astounding fossil: the huge jawbone, which still contained one tooth, of "the great antediluvial animal the Megatherium." This was an extinct species closely related to the sloth; it had stood twenty feet high.

When Darwin returned to the ship with his precious cargo of bones, Captain Fitzroy declared that they belonged to animals that had failed to get into Noah's Ark! Darwin, however, had very different thoughts. Careful examination showed him that the fossil head belonged to an extinct creature known as a Toxodon, and a curious creature it was. Although it was fully as big as an elephant, the Toxodon was actually a giant member of the rodent family that had lived at the end of the Tertiary period. Oddly enough, he noticed, it bore a distant resemblance to a modern South American rodent known as a capybara, which stands about two feet high and is about four feet long. Even the Megatherium, for all its monstrous size, had a counterpart in the present-day South American sloth, although modern sloths are barely three feet high.

To Darwin, it seemed extremely curious that God, the Creator of species, should have placed these modern sloths and capybaras exactly where, during the Tertiary period, He had previously placed the extinct giant sloth and the extinct giant Toxodon. Was there a reason, Darwin later wondered, why the creative force had done this? Was there a reason, that is, why God had replaced two ancient species

OVERLEAF: *Powerfully excited by his first glimpse of tropical jungle, and the lush profusion depicted here by a Frenchman long resident in Brazil, Darwin wrote: "The brilliancy of the scenery throws one into a delirium of delight." To the end of his life he maintained that he had felt his most sublime emotion in these forests.*
DEBRET, *Voyage . . . au Brésil*, 1834: N.Y. PUBLIC LIBRARY

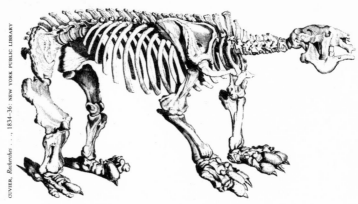

On a Patagonian beach Darwin unearthed the tooth-studded jaw-bone (above) of a giant Megatherium (top, right), South America's largest mammal during the Pleistocene age and the ancestor of the modern sloth. At top left, a mother and baby demonstrate a truly slothful ability to sleep endlessly without moving at all.

by two modern ones that slightly resembled them? Must he say, as other naturalists did, that this was the will of God and therefore not to be queried? Darwin had as yet no answers to such questions.

To sharpen his curiosity even more, he had made yet another interesting discovery at Punta Alta. On the very day he found the Megatherium jawbone, he came upon a poisonous snake—a kind of viper—that made a rattling sound as it slithered through the grass. This was odd, thought Darwin, for vipers do not have rattles as rattlesnakes do. Looking more closely (for when it came to gathering facts, he was quite fearless), he saw that this particular snake belonged to a species whose tail was curiously hardened at the tip. By brushing its tail against the grass as it traveled, the snake made the sound that Darwin had heard. What the viper possessed, he noted, was a simpler kind of noisemaker, not so highly developed as the marvelous rattling tail of the rattlesnake.

Here again was something to arouse his curiosity. It was impossible to doubt that the Creator of species had given each rattlesnake an elaborate and beautifully contrived device for warning off its enemies. But why had the same creative force bestowed a crude kind of noisemaker on another species of snake? Was it possible—did Darwin dare to believe—that this particular species had somehow developed a hardened tail tip all by itself? Could a species change in this way? The thought was almost blasphemous, for it meant denying that God had created each separate living thing individually. It would also be generally considered as scientifically absurd, and Darwin was not the kind of man to leap to conclusions over a few isolated facts.

Such vague and troubled thoughts as these would soon open fresh pathways for Darwin, but at the moment the only path he was keenly aware of was that of the *Beagle*. It was now sailing north again, back to the River Plate, much to his regret. Considering that the ship had the whole world yet to circumnavigate, it was disheartening, he thought, to have to take backward steps, even in order to take on fresh supplies. His home in Shrewsbury seemed a long way off. Even the seasons in South America were reversed. By the time Darwin reached Montevideo in the late spring month of November, 1832, he had been on the *Beagle* for almost a year and was suffering from an acute case of homesickness. "On board the ship all goes on as well as possible," he wrote Henslow, to whom he was sending a consignment of specimens. "The only drawback is the fearful length of time between this and the day of our return. I do not see any limits to it."

Still, he had no intention of quitting, although the thought crossed his mind. If he quit, he wrote his sister Catherine, "I don't think I should ever rest quiet in my grave. I certainly should be a ghost and haunt the British Museum." He was becoming more conscious all the time of the value of his scientific work. Darwin had ceased to be a mere collector of specimens. He had already begun to ask himself serious theoretical questions, and now he wanted to find out the answers for himself. As he wrote to Catherine in June, 1833, "It appears to me the doing of what *little* we can to increase the general stock of knowledge is as respectable an object in life as one can in any likelihood pursue." It was a gentle hint to his family that he intended to become a scientist. Dr. Darwin had been right: the trip aboard the *Beagle* had unfitted his son for the profession of clergyman.

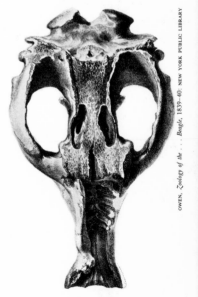

Finding the fossil skull (above) of a Toxodon, a Pleistocene mammal as big as a rhinoceros, Darwin noted its similarity to the four-foot-long capybaras (left) that still inhabit South America.

47

NATURALIST

Jean-Baptiste Debret, a Frenchman living in Brazil, depicted South America as a naturalist's paradise. Here, one scientist's servants bring in some colorful specimens, including a live sloth riding piggyback (at center).

IN SOUTH AMERICA

During the early months of 1833 the *Beagle* sailed all the way south to Tierra del Fuego and back, a twenty-five-hundred-mile round trip that left Charles Darwin once again at the River Plate. The Tierra del Fuego visit was made to bring Fitzroy's three "civilized" Fuegians—York Minster and his intended bride, Fuegia Basket, and Jemmy Button—back to their homeland at the tip of the continent and to establish a mission among the savage, cannibalistic Fuegians.

It was a strange and pathetic homecoming, especially for Jemmy Button, the ship's favorite. A plump, lively fellow, Jemmy wore a natty English suit and highly polished shoes. Darwin observed how he loved to stare at himself in the looking glass, admiring his unusual new costume. The outfit must have seemed exceedingly strange to Jemmy, since he belonged to a tribe that wore no clothes at all. His people, the Yaghans, were among the most primitive in the world, so it was a matter of great curiosity to all the *Beagle*'s crew to see how the Yaghans would welcome their newly civilized tribesman.

The great day came in January, 1833, when the *Beagle* finally located the island on which Jemmy's own family lived. With his shipboard friends to accompany him, Jemmy came on shore to greet his relatives, but they just stood and stared at him silently. Jemmy stared silently back. Nobody made a move. Here was Jemmy, dressed up like an English gentleman, and there, a few feet away, was his brother, dirty and completely naked, his hair growing wild and his face streaked with red and white paint.

Finally, Jemmy said a few words—in English! It was gibberish, of course, to his brother. Jemmy tried again, this time in Spanish. "*¿No sabe?*" he asked his brother, "Don't you understand?" Poor Jemmy Button! He had forgotten the sounds of his native language. Three years of learning English, gardening, and what Fitzroy called "plainer Christianity" had made him a misfit among his own people.

*Captain Fitzroy made these draw-
ings of his Fuegian protégés in
European dress, after he brought
them to England in 1830. The dap-
per Jemmy Button is at top, with
Fuegia Basket between him and
her future husband, York Minster.*

The *Beagle*'s crew spent several days planting gardens
and building huts to house the English missionary and the
other two Fuegians, who had decided to settle in the same
area as Jemmy. The natives crowded around, watching,
begging for gifts, and stealing whatever they could. The
women helped with the work, while the men lounged about,
gossiping. Once the little settlement was established, the
Beagle set off to do some more surveying, since everything
seemed friendly and peaceful.

On the ship's return, barely ten days later, Captain
Fitzroy found complete chaos. Every one of the missionary's
possessions had been stolen, and the natives had turned him
out of his hut and even threatened his life. Fitzroy had no
choice but to abandon the idea of converting the natives
and take the badly frightened man back on board. York,
Fuegia, and Jemmy stayed behind, although they too had
lost most of their belongings. In bewilderment, Jemmy admitted that his own family had been the ringleaders in strip-
ping the group of their civilized possessions.

By this time, Darwin may have felt a little like Jemmy
Button himself. While Jemmy's civilized clothes had con-
cealed his true Yaghan identity from his fellow tribesmen,
so Darwin's cheerful, boyish manner now cloaked his rebel-
lious mind from those around him. Had he known Darwin's
thoughts, Captain Fitzroy would have thought them bor-
dering on blasphemy. To the ship's officers, however, Darwin was still the "dear old philosopher" who cluttered the
decks with his specimens and quoted the Bible to settle
points of dispute. To the captain he was still a pleasant shipboard dinner companion who could amuse him during the
evenings with adventurous tales of South American frontier
life.

Darwin had much to tell, for in April, 1833, he had explored the rugged cattle region north of the River Plate,
now known as Uruguay. It was lawless country, where the
roads were marked with crosses and each cross indicated
where a murder had been committed. With thieves and
bandits lurking everywhere, Darwin noted in his diary,
"your entire safety in this country depends on your companions." Fortunately, his guides were both well armed
and loyal.

In August, 1833, Darwin found himself in an even more
forbidding region, the huge southern province of Argentina
known as Patagonia. He was set ashore at the mouth of the
Río Negro, the southernmost outpost of civilization on the
eastern coast of South America, to explore the treeless

Darwin employed two Uruguayan guides like these, with twelve horses, for the small sum of two dollars a day. Although fierce and well armed, down to knives in their boots, they were devoted to "el naturalista Don Carlos."

gravelly desert country while the *Beagle* carried on survey work off the coast. With five Gauchos, a guide, and another Englishman for company, Darwin at once set off on a geological expedition to Bahía Blanca, two hundred miles to the north, and then traveled an additional three hundred miles to Buenos Aires. It was a rough excursion, through Indian country, and the members of the party had nothing to eat but the game they could shoot with their rifles. At night they slept on their saddle packs, while vultures watched them patiently from every surrounding hill. Darwin thoroughly enjoyed himself. "I am become quite a Gaucho," he wrote to his sister Caroline, "drink my Mattee [maté, a kind of tea] & smoke my cigar, & then lie down & sleep as comfortably with the Heavens for canopy, as in a feather bed. It is such a fine healthy life; on horse-back all day, eating nothing but meat, & sleeping in a bracing air, one awakes as fresh as a lark."

Yet it was science, not scenery, that excited Darwin now. At the Río Negro, Gauchos told him of a rare species of ostrich, called *avestruz Petise*, that lived on the plains of

51

Patagonia. Immediately his interest was fired. He knew well enough that ostriches, or rheas, as the South American species are called, abounded farther north in Argentina. He had galloped after them himself and seen how the Gauchos captured them—by tangling up their powerful legs with a skillfully thrown bola (a leather cord weighted at both ends) —and then killed them to make a savory supper. But although he was constantly on the alert, Darwin could not find any trace of the legendary *Petise* as he traveled over the Patagonian desert.

The long expedition was nevertheless a most valuable one. While traveling so many miles across Argentina, Darwin found strong evidence that the accepted theory of geological catastrophes was false and that Lyell's controversial theory of a gradual evolution must be the correct one. His careful examination of the rocks and the formation of the country over which they traveled had shown him no evidence that any titanic catastrophe had ever taken place in Argentina. He could only conclude that this gravelly piece of the earth's crust must have been formed, as he said, "slowly and gradually" over millions of years. This was a conclusion of profound importance to Darwin's whole train of thought. If the geologist were to establish that the earth in its present form had evolved, without supernatural aid, over a period of countless millions of years, why should not the biologist reject the idea of separate and individual creation of each species? Was it not possible for God to have created the most primitive forms of life and set them on earth to develop, in a sense, by themselves?

Early in 1834, when the *Beagle* began its final survey of the Argentine coast, two more significant discoveries came Darwin's way. Since the previous year he had been employing, at his own expense, a lad named Simms Covington, who acted as his assistant. Covington had begun his trip on the *Beagle* as "ship's fiddler and boy to the poop cabin," but Fitzroy had allowed him to change jobs. By teaching the boy to shoot and to skin and stuff birds, Darwin had gained

The French artist Debret sketched a traveler on the South American Pampas, resting at night. Still in his hat, he snoozes under a blanket hanging from an intricately built stockade. The corral-shaped structure is made out of supply boxes topped by his mules' pack saddles.

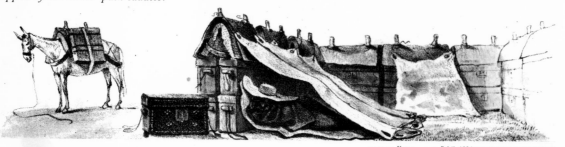

ATLANTIC
OCEAN

VENEZUELA

GUIANA

COLOMBIA

Galapagos
Islands

EQUATOR

ECUADOR

Amazon River

PERU

BRAZIL

Callao •Lima

Bahia

BOLIVIA

PARAGUAY

Rio de Janeiro

TROPIC OF
CAPRICORN

CHILE

ARGENTINA

River Plate

URUGUAY

Valparaiso

Buenos
Aires

Montevideo

PACIFIC
OCEAN

Rio Negro

Bahia Blanca

Patagonia

Port
St. Julian

Falkland
Islands

This map of South America
indicates the *Beagle*'s major
ports of call on her voyage
around the continent, lasting
from 1832 to 1835. The line
linking the ports shows the
general direction in which
the vessel sailed but omits
the many retraced steps that
made the three-year survey
so exhausting for her crew.

Tierra
del Fuego

much free time for research. At a desolate spot on the Patagonian shore Covington brought in a small ostrich one of the crew had killed. "I looked at it," Darwin recalled later, "forgetting at the moment, in the most unaccountable manner, the whole subject of the *Petises*, and thought it was a not full-grown bird of the common sort."

That day the crew of the *Beagle* sat down to a pleasant dinner of ostrich meat. Only later did Darwin's memory awaken with a start. He had just eaten the rare *avestruz Petise*! He raced to the ship's galley and arrived in time to salvage the bird's head, neck, wings, legs, and feathers. With these inedible portions he managed to assemble the type specimen of this previously unknown species (which was later named *Rhea darwini* in his honor). The Gauchos, he could now see for himself, had been quite correct—the rare *Petise* was a distinct species of ostrich, which looked very much like the common ostrich. Pondering the significance of this, Darwin found it hard to believe that the creative force could have placed this second type of ostrich so close to the common ostrich for no reason at all. There had to be a better and more scientific explanation.

The second piece in the complicated jigsaw puzzle he was now putting together fell into his hands a few days later. The *Beagle* sailed south to Port St. Julian, close to the tip of the South American mainland, and here Darwin found half a skeleton of an extinct camel-like creature known as a Macrauchenia. After examining this specimen, Darwin realized that this extinct creature too had a modern counterpart in the area. Living camel-like animals known as guanacos travel in large herds all over Patagonia.

Here was yet another of those curious resemblances between extinct species and living species in the same general area. There was the dead Toxodon and the present-day capybara, the giant Megatherium and the present-day sloth. A few months before he had found fossil remains of a giant armor-plated creature that bore a fairly close resemblance to living South America armadillos. Now he had found Macrauchenia in the very place where the guanaco herds grazed.

As Darwin turned these findings over in his mind in the following months, he became convinced that they were not coincidental, isolated facts, but facts that were falling into a pattern. "This wonderful relationship between the living and the dead," he called it. To Darwin, such a pattern of facts cried out for an explanation. The catastrophists had an explanation, but it no longer satisfied him.

Classifying this avestruz Petise, *ornithologist John Gould named it* Rhea darwini *for Darwin.*

According to the accepted view, God had introduced the modern species after unleashing a catastrophe that had killed off the Tertiary species. But why, Darwin could now ask, had the creative force in Argentina so often replaced the extinct species with new ones that resembled them? Why had it not replaced them with entirely different modern species? Why should there be any resemblance at all? What was more, Darwin now had good reason to doubt there had ever been a catastrophe in Argentina in the first place. If the whole theory of catastrophes was wrong, there must be some other explanation for this astonishing resemblance between the living and the dead.

He could say, echoing his grandfather, that the modern capybaras, sloths, and armadillos had descended from the extinct species that resembled them. Yet how, after all, could he or anybody else believe this? First of all, it was impossible to conceive how a species could change, and sec-

Swinging his bola above his head, an Argentinian Gaucho speeds after a fleeing ostrich. In a minute, he will cast the heavily weighted cord and bring the bird down by hobbling its legs. The task requires great skill, as Darwin found when he caught his bola in a bush and hobbled the horse he was riding instead of the ostrich.

VIDAL, *Picturesque Illustrations of Buenos Ayres*, 1820: NEW YORK PUBLIC LIBRARY

As the Beagle *worked slowly north along the Peruvian coast, the impressionable Darwin visited Lima and noted that the capital's elegant ladies, like this provocative damsel, half covered their faces with silk mantillas but left exposed an eye "so black and brilliant . . . that its effect is very powerful."*

ondly, every reputable scientist denied that such a change was possible. Was it reasonable to believe that the twenty-foot-high Megatherium had shrunk into a three-foot sloth? The Tertiary species were giants, while the modern species, said Darwin, were pygmies. No, he decided, it was just as hard to believe in Erasmus Darwin's ideas about evolution as it was to believe in catastrophes. There was only one thing he was sure of. There had to be some natural explanation for this puzzling pattern of facts.

On September 15, 1835, almost four years after the *Beagle* had sailed from England, the ship put into the remote Galápagos Islands, six hundred miles into the Pacific from the mainland of South America. Here Darwin was to come face to face with the mystery of the origin of species.

On Chatham Island, one of the five larger islands in the Galápagos chain of ten, Darwin found himself at one of the strangest places on earth. Situated far from any mainland, the Galápagos Islands existed—and still exist—in deep and rarely disturbed isolation from the rest of the world. Chatham itself, Darwin noted, was as bleak as the traditional picture of the moon. As he climbed over black volcanic rocks, he had to push aside "disgusting clumsy lizards" that crawled and swarmed over the beach. So few men had set foot in the Galápagos that the animals had absolutely no fear of man. Approaching a hawk that sat perched on a tree branch, Darwin simply pushed it off the branch with the barrel of his gun. Here, too, he saw the famed tortoises of the Galápagos Islands, giant, slow-moving creatures with shells three feet in diameter. They seemed to Darwin like inhabitants of another planet. Indeed, the entire archipelago resembled a piece of another world, for its plants and animals were unlike those of any other place. The creative force, it seemed, had created them especially for these remote and dreary rocks.

Yet Darwin, on his second day of exploration, noticed something quite different. As he tersely commented in his diary: "I certainly recognize South America in ornithology." He meant that the Galápagos birds bore a distant resemblance to the birds of South America. If the creative force had created these birds especially for the Galápagos Islands, it had modeled them on "American types of organization." But if these creatures resembled South American birds, by far the most likely probability was that they had come from South America, six hundred miles away.

The significance of this thought was truly staggering, for Darwin knew that these birds were not found in South

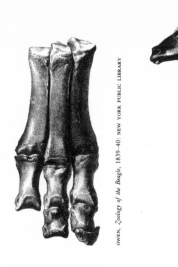

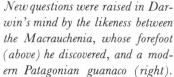

New questions were raised in Darwin's mind by the likeness between the Macrauchenia, whose forefoot (above) he discovered, and a modern Patagonian guanaco (right).

America; they merely had a slight resemblance to South American birds. They were alike and yet different, and there was, he now came to think, an explanation for this fact, difficult as it was to imagine. It was possible that a long time ago the ancestors of these Galápagos birds had come to the islands from South America. Here they had lived, completely cut off from their brothers on the mainland. Living in isolation, they had gradually changed into the unique species that he saw around him. They resembled South American birds because they originally came from South America. They were found only in the Galápagos Islands because they had changed into new species by themselves while living on these islands!

With intense excitement, Darwin began collecting bird specimens as the *Beagle* moved quickly from one island to another, surveying and charting each one. Here, he knew, was the opportunity of his lifetime. In the splendid isolation of the Galápagos Islands, under a blazing tropical sun, nature was revealing a secret for the first time. What he now found turned his new hypothesis into a profound and unshakable conviction.

What he found, oddly enough, was a group of little finches as dull-looking in plumage as any birds could be. They are now deservedly called "Darwin's finches," and they helped to change the whole course of human thought.

OVERLEAF: *In this strange landscape, typical of the Galápagos Islands, where reptiles were the highest form of native life, Darwin felt he approached "that mystery of mysteries—the first appearance of new beings on this earth."*
RUDOLPH FREUND

These finches, found only on the Galápagos Islands, were divided, Darwin found, into thirteen different species. This was a large number for such a small area. What was more astonishing, there was almost no difference between them save in the size of their beaks. Some species had small, sharp beaks, others had medium-sized beaks, and a few species had beaks that looked as formidable as those of parrots. Here was an amazing array of living things, unexceptional as they were at first glance. For when each species was set alongside the others, they really looked, said Darwin, like a single finch species that had been "taken and modified for different ends." With that observation, he had come to the end of the lonely road he had been traveling for so long.

He could no longer believe that God had separately created each of these thirteen species of finch, thirteen species that looked so much alike. The finches could only be the descendants of some South American finch, the ancestral finch that had migrated long ago to the islands. There on the empty archipelago, living in utter isolation, the finches of countless succeeding generations had gradually developed beaks of different sizes for use in gathering the different types of food to be found on each island. The thirteen separate species had not been created; they had evolved by themselves!

True, it was impossible to imagine how this transformation had taken place, but when Darwin looked at those finches, he knew that the transformation had actually occurred. Thirteen new species of living things had come into

Landing in a rocky cove on Chatham Island (above), the Beagle's *crew found the air oppressively hot. "We fancied even that the bushes smelt unpleasantly," wrote Darwin. On Charles Island (right), a few Spanish colonists scraped a living by growing sweet potatoes and bananas in the moist soil.*

existence because their ancestors had slowly and gradually changed. If this was true of the finches, it must be true of other living things. The two ostrich species were probably descended from a common ostrich ancestor, whose offspring evolved in two different directions. The modern sloths and capybaras were descendants of more ancient sloths and rodents. They too had not been individually created. They too had evolved by themselves.

At last the *Beagle* made for home, carrying its impatient crew across the Pacific and Indian oceans, around South Africa's Cape of Good Hope, and into the Atlantic once more. Aboard, in Darwin's carefully kept diary and his twenty-four little field notebooks, were the raw materials for a theory that would one day shake the world.

It is impossible to say whether he was delighted or not with his new and revolutionary hypothesis. It was a hypothesis with a gaping flaw: it was still as impossible as ever to understand *how* a species could change. That such change had occurred he doubted no longer, but the cause of this transmutation—a transmutation that nobody had ever seen and that everybody denied could occur—he could not explain. The problem, he said, haunted him; he was not yet ready to cheer.

There is no doubt, however, how Darwin felt on October 2, 1836. On that day, four years and nine months from the day it had sailed, the battered little *Beagle* dropped anchor at Falmouth, in Cornwall. A homesick Darwin, preparing to journey nonstop to Shrewsbury by mail coach, was then a very happy man indeed.

Pitted by craters (above) and washed by Antarctic currents, the equatorial Galápagos Islands are unique. Their name comes from the giant tortoise, or galápago (top, second from left), which is found nowhere else. Also peculiar to the islands are the swarms of marine iguanas (left), which feed on underwater seaweed. Comparing them with the land iguana (top, far left), Darwin marveled at finding two such similar species in "so confined a portion of the world." Cataloguing the birds, he found twelve species allied to the seed-eating finch (second from right), but with varying sizes of beaks. Although the land birds lacked any protection, unlike the camouflaged baby penguins at top right, they were all so tame that Darwin realized that until man's coming they had had no natural enemies.

63

IV

NATURAL SELECTION: KEY TO A THEORY

On a July day in 1837, nine months after Darwin's happy homecoming, the young world traveler sat in his London lodgings on Great Marlborough Street with his diary in front of him. "In July opened first notebook," he wrote, "on Transmutation of Species." Then he added, as if to explain to himself what he was doing: "Had been greatly struck from about Month of previous March on character of S. American fossils—and species on Galapagos Archipelago. These facts origin (especially latter) of all my views." In the notebook he intended to collect all the facts he could find bearing on the question of the origin of species. In this modest manner, at the age of twenty-eight, Charles Darwin commenced his life's great work.

Fortunately there was little to distract him. In the months since his return everything had been going extremely well, far better than he had ever expected. He had come home to find himself looked upon as a highly promising young naturalist. Henslow had circulated his letters from the *Beagle*, and Darwin's own enthusiasm and his enormous collections of specimens reinforced the favorable impression the letters had made among England's leading scientists. He had already delivered two scientific papers, one to the Zoological Society on the South American ostrich, or rhea, and one to the Geological Society, of which he was now a member, on evidence he had found of volcanic upthrusting of the land along the Chilean coastline.

Best of all, he had instantly struck up a warm friendship with Charles Lyell, whose treatise on geology had been his

While on the Beagle, *Darwin collected as many insect species as possible, trying not to favor one order more than another. These beetles from just one order, Coleoptera, bear tribute to his industry and acute observation.*

Mid-nineteenth-century London offered social as well as intellectual diversions. The hub of the fashionable world was Hyde Park (above), where elegant socialites went on carriage outings or joined their friends for a leisurely stroll.

guide throughout the *Beagle* voyage. Lyell himself had been following Darwin's adventures and reports with eager interest. "How I long for the return of Darwin!" he wrote to Professor Sedgwick in December, 1835, and almost as soon as the *Beagle* docked, Lyell was offering his young colleague help and advice. At once, he and Darwin began the free-ranging discussion and exchange of theories that was to make their long and ungrudging friendship so fruitful.

COURTESY OF B. WEINREB PRINTS AND MAPS LTD., LONDON

Young Darwin had taken rooms a few doors away from his brother, Erasmus, who had long since abandoned any ideas of taking on Dr. Darwin's medical practice and was living a carefree bachelor existence in London. Thanks to him, Charles led an active social life in literary as well as scientific circles. Erasmus was particularly friendly with the great historian Thomas Carlyle, and Darwin used to enjoy telling of a dinner party given by his brother, attended by,

67

among others, Carlyle, Lyell, a distinguished mathematician named Charles Babbage, and Charles himself. Both Babbage and Lyell liked to talk but never got a word in, since Carlyle "silenced every one by haranguing during the whole dinner on the advantages of silence. After dinner, Babbage, in his grimmest manner, thanked Carlyle for his very interesting Lecture on Silence."

By the end of summer Darwin had completed a soon-to-be published book, an account of his travels with the *Beagle*, based on the scientific diaries he had kept on the voyage. This accomplishment was a special delight to him. "If I live till I am eighty years old," he wrote to Henslow, "I shall not cease to marvel at finding myself an author." As he remarked half-jokingly, praise from the "great guns" of science was beginning to turn his head. "I feel too often like a peacock admiring his tail," he confided to his cousin William Fox, in July, 1837. Friendly, modest, and frank, Darwin had nothing in common with a peacock. But a man who plans to overthrow an entire system of scientific thought needs all the self-confidence he can muster. The preceding nine months had given Darwin "much confidence," he admitted, "and I hope not a very great deal of vanity."

The difficulties before him, however, were enormous and baffling. Darwin knew he could not simply trumpet the idea of evolution and expect the fortress of orthodox science to crumble at the sound. To most scientists, evolution was a fairly old and a thoroughly discredited idea. Those to whom Darwin confided his theory thought he was wasting his time, and they politely told him so. "Scarcely any novelty in my theory," Darwin jotted down glumly in his "transmutation" notebook, "only slight differences, the opinion of many people in conversation." As far as Darwin's scientific colleagues were concerned, he was flogging a dead horse. The latest advances of science, they believed, had definitely shown all the existing theories about evolution to be absurd, unfounded, and unscientific.

In 1794 few geological theories had been formulated and little was known about fossils and what forms of life they actually represented. Thus it had been relatively easy for Erasmus Darwin, Charles' grandfather, to suggest that all living things might have descended from one original prototype. Even in 1809—the year of Charles' birth—it was still relatively easy for another evolutionist, a Frenchman named Jean-Baptiste de Lamarck, to outline in detail a similar theory of "transformism." According to this theory, every animal that was "low" on the scale of nature, as it

This Wedgwood platter is decorated with plant motifs selected from Dr. Erasmus Darwin's popular poem "Loves of the Plants," which contained some of his unorthodox ideas about evolution.

French botanist Jean-Baptiste de Lamarck, shown here in old age, was misled by studying the close resemblances between related species into believing that species could evolve by transforming themselves into "higher" forms of life.

was called, had an innate tendency to transform itself gradually into a "higher" and "more perfect" creature. Over long periods of time a fish, by Lamarck's theory, would naturally tend to become a reptile. The reptile had the same innate tendency to become a mammal, which was in turn destined by nature to become a human being. The obvious gaps and imperfections in the scale Lamarck attributed to the effects of adaptation by species to their environment instead of to the ideal.

By 1837, however, scientists knew too much about the structure and classification of species to credit such vague and general ideas. Lamarck's scale of nature, whereby all animal species were arranged from lowest to highest as if they were numbers in a row, had been discredited by Georges Cuvier's painstaking work on fossil remains. Cuvier's remarkable knowledge of anatomy enabled him to replace the traditional idea of a scale by dividing all the species of the animal world into four distinct and fundamental groups known as phyla. (Later scientists have divided these groups still further into some twenty phyla.)

Cuvier's groups included the phylum of species with backbones, known as vertebrate animals, and also the phylum of species whose bodies are formed in segments, such as worms, insects, crabs, and lobsters. A species in one phylum is so different from one in any other phylum that it is meaningless to say that one is lower or higher than the other. In what way is the segmented lobster "lower" than the vertebrate codfish? Since the scale of nature was the basis of Lamarck's entire theory, its rejection by the scientists who followed Cuvier left "transformism" without a foundation. Indeed, the new classification seemed to weaken all evolutionary speculations. It was impossible to imagine how a segmented lobster, for example, could ever change into the most primitive creature with a spine. Each phylum seemed like a separate world within the larger world of living things.

Other arguments were hurled against the idea of evolution. There was, of course, the fundamental fact that nobody had ever seen or heard of a species changing. But the strongest argument of all was based on an entirely different set of facts, which were about living things themselves. These particular facts not only made evolution impossible to believe; they also inspired scientists with an unshakable conviction that God had created each individual species.

It must be remembered that Darwin's faith in his new theory rested on his belief that it could explain many facts of biology better than "creationism," as he called the or-

An 1841 edition of Buffon's Book
of Birds *illustrates woodpeckers
from Europe (1), Santo Domingo
(2), and French Guiana (3).
Each has the strutlike tail, sharp
beak, and feet on which two toes
point backward that make this
species ideally adapted to live
on grubs obtained by hammering
through the tough bark of trees.*

thodox theory. The Galápagos finches and the resemblance
between Tertiary period fossils and living South American
species were the key facts he had found so far. He fully expected to find other patterns of facts that could be explained
more satisfactorily by evolution than by creationism. Such
facts Darwin called indirect evidence for his theory. Unfortunately, he was as yet quite unable to explain the particular pattern of facts that was supremely important to the
creationists. This was the circumstance that each living
thing is superbly adapted to the mode of life that it leads.

The classic illustration of adaptation is the common
woodpecker, which was Darwin's own favorite example.
The woodpecker lives on grubs and insects, which it reaches
by pecking through the bark of trees. To accomplish this
task, the woodpecker is equipped not only with a pointed
beak for penetrating the bark, but also with an extremely
long tongue for snatching the grubs that live within. What
is more remarkable, the woodpecker's head is specially constructed to withstand the pressure of its hammering, and
two toes on each foot point backward so that it can get a
firmer grip on the tree trunk. A long stiff tail, which acts as

a prop, enables the bird to stay upright while pecking. The woodpecker, it is obvious to any observer, is admirably designed for the particular life it leads.

Such adaptations, which abound in nature, formed one of the strongest foundation stones of the entire creationist theory. In 1802 William Paley, an English clergyman, published his *Natural Theology*, which at once became required reading for naturalists and theologians alike (and greatly impressed Darwin himself when he was assigned it at Cambridge). In it Paley put forward the theory that precisely *because* every living species was so cunningly adapted to its environment, each of them must have been created by God. A formless heap of granite might have piled up by accident, but a heap of granite formed into a beautiful castle must have been the work of an intelligent builder. Since each living species was so well suited for life in the environment in which it had been placed, it must have been specially made for that environment. "The marks of design are too strong to be gotten over," wrote Paley. "Design must have had a designer. That designer must have been a person. That person is God." He then took his argument a stage further, insisting that God had chosen to make these exquisitely complicated adaptations in order to demonstrate in scientific terms the extent of His wisdom and power.

Confronted with the facts of adaptation, Darwin was trapped. On one hand, his theory had to explain how a primitive creature could evolve into a living species that was perfectly adapted to its environment. He must show that a species that looked exactly as if it had been designed by an all-powerful Creator could in fact be produced by a process of evolution. On the other hand, Darwin strongly believed, a truly scientific theory of evolution must not say, as Lamarck's and Erasmus Darwin's did, that the evolution of species was guided by some innate tendency to produce the species that live today. He was not prepared to say, for example, that the ancestor of the tiger developed stripes because it was destined eventually to become a tiger or because it had "wanted" to become a tiger. Such explanations did not really explain anything; it was like saying that bodies fall to the center of the earth because they have an innate tendency to do so, or because they "want" to do so.

Darwin was convinced from the moment he began his research that a scientific theory of evolution could not depend on such vague explanations. All he could say was that each tiny change in the ancestor of the tiger must have happened by accident and without any particular purpose.

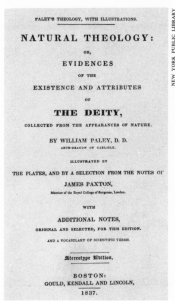

PALEY'S THEOLOGY, WITH ILLUSTRATIONS.

NATURAL THEOLOGY:

OR,

EVIDENCES

OF THE

EXISTENCE AND ATTRIBUTES

OF

THE DEITY,

COLLECTED FROM THE APPEARANCES OF NATURE.

BY WILLIAM PALEY, D. D.

ARCH-DEACON OF CARLISLE.

ILLUSTRATED BY

THE PLATES, AND BY A SELECTION FROM THE NOTES OF

JAMES PAXTON,

Member of the Royal College of Surgeons, London.

WITH

ADDITIONAL NOTES,

ORIGINAL AND SELECTED, FOR THIS EDITION.

AND A VOCABULARY OF SCIENTIFIC TERMS.

Stereotype Edition.

BOSTON:

GOULD, KENDALL AND LINCOLN,

1837.

Thirty-five years after the Rev. William Paley (above) first published his famous treatise, Natural Theology, *the book was still so popular on both sides of the Atlantic that a Boston publisher issued a revised edition (bottom).*

NATIONAL AUDUBON SOCIETY: PHOTO, CHARLES J. OTT

Adaptation to environment is one of the marvels of nature. Darwin's problem was to prove how it could be the result of countless tiny changes that gave a species a better chance of survival. For protection against predators, the snowshoe hare above changes the color of its fur from brown to white to match the seasons in its native Arctic. Near right, a crab spider (top) protects itself by a body structure imitating the buds of the creosote bush, while the walking stick (center) and deadleaf butterfly (bottom) are identical with the dry twigs and dead leaves where they live. Far right, a beaver (top) is camouflaged from enemies by a coat the color of the reeds around his fishing pond. The copperhead snake (center) has two defenses: leaflike coloration and deadly poison fangs. At bottom, a sandy-speckled flounder burrows for protection into the sea floor.

Some species protect themselves not by adaptive coloration but by mimicking a species that an enemy will not dare attack. The Caligo butterfly (above) has developed markings underneath its wings that resemble the eyes of an owl (below). These scare off birds that enjoy eating butterflies but are frightened of owls.

Over a hundred thousand generations or more, these accidental changes in the color of the ancestral tiger's fur added up, somehow, to a striped coat. But since the process of evolution resulted in living things that were beautifully adapted to their environment, the baffling problem for Darwin was this: He had to show how a great many random, purposeless changes could eventually bring about a creature that looked exactly as if it had been designed on purpose. On the face of it, this was like believing that rocks rolling down a hill could pile up by themselves into a castle!

"This really perhaps greatest difficulty," Darwin admitted frankly in the privacy of his notebook. "I had always been much struck by such adaptations," he later recalled, "and until these could be explained it seemed to me almost useless to endeavour to prove by indirect evidence [the Galápagos finches for example] that species have been modified." If he could not find the cause of evolutionary change and show how this cause could produce species adapted to their environment, then the theory of evolution, Darwin thought, was not worth believing. "To say that all mammals were born from one stock and since distributed by such means as we can recognize," he acknowledged, "may be thought to explain nothing."

In exactly fifteen months from the day he began his work, Darwin solved these fundamental problems and discovered the splendidly simple key to evolution.

He began this truly extraordinary period simply by turning upside down a central fact of biology. This fact was the well-known resemblance between parents and their offspring. Darwin did not deny, of course, that children resembled their parents. But it was equally true, as he saw at once, that they never resembled them exactly. There was always "variation," as he called it, between parents and children, and between the several children of the same parents. "Wild animals," he noted in his telegraphic style, "vary exceedingly little, yet they are known as individuals." Many of these small variations were hereditary, meaning that they were passed on from the variant child to his own children. Darwin had no doubt that these tiny variations were the little building blocks through which the great changes of evolution had been produced. The accumulation of these extremely small variations between one generation and the next must slowly add up until, after thousands of generations had gone by, the descendants of the original parents were so completely different from them that they had come to constitute an entirely new species.

Here, however, Darwin was stopped in his tracks. A child, for example, might have a somewhat larger nose than either of his parents, and his child might have a larger nose than he had. But as the generations passed, the members of this family would not indefinitely continue to inherit larger and larger noses. Even after a dozen generations the inherited family nose would never grow larger than a recognizable human-sized nose. To make this point even more telling, Charles Lyell, in his *Principles of Geology*, had offered a powerful argument to show just why these tiny variations could *not* grow larger and larger over the generations.

Lyell's argument was Darwin's great road block, and it went as follows: Suppose, for example, that the offspring of a woodpecker is somewhat unlike its parents. Since everyone agrees that the woodpecker is perfectly adapted to its environment, this variant child, being different, must be less perfectly adapted than its parents.

At this point in the argument Lyell introduced an idea that his young friend Darwin would soon put to exactly the opposite use. Lyell called it "the struggle for existence." Staying alive in nature is not easy, as Lyell showed in some detail. Every plant and animal is preyed upon by its natural enemies. Food is often scarce. Nature is no place for weaklings. A sad fate awaits this poor, imperfect child of the woodpecker: He very likely will not survive the struggle for

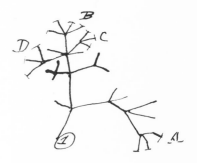

Extracts from Darwin's notebooks on transmutation reveal his mind at work. The evolutionary tree above starts with an original ancestor (1) and letters the branches that have produced surviving species. The page below poses such questions as (first line): Did Eyton's hybrids, when interbred, show any tendency to return to either parent? Penciled notes show he incorporated this material into his larger book in 1856.

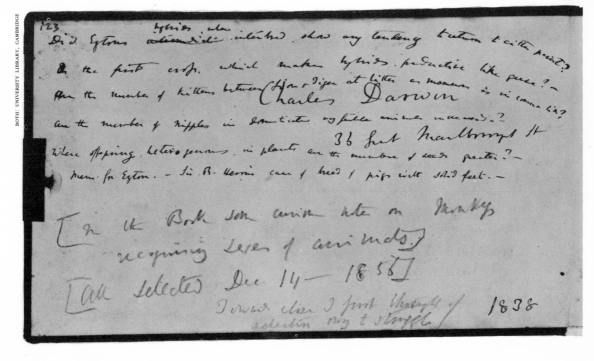

existence. However, his brothers and sisters, who resemble their parents closely and thus are as well adapted as they, will live to maturity and produce the next generation of "normal" woodpeckers. This is the reason, said Lyell, that species can never change. The struggle for existence mercilessly weeds out every single offspring that differs from its parents, because it is imperfect and hence it is too weak to survive.

Reading this argument in Lyell's book, Darwin scribbled a jaunty comment in the margin: "If this were true, *adios* theory." Good-by evolution, indeed! If all the variant children of a parent were mercilessly killed off, then evolution would be impossible, as Lyell himself firmly believed.

About this time—that is, during the first few months of Darwin's research—various English cattle raisers, gardeners, and pigeon fanciers found themselves confronted by a most inquisitive young man who plied them with questions about their work. This visitor, of course, was Darwin, going off on a wholly new tack in his researches. He had decided to investigate change in living things in the only areas where it was known and universally admitted to occur: in the experimental gardens and farms where domesticated animals and plants were being scientifically bred.

Rosa Indica (left), a five-petaled wild rose from the Orient, was imported into England in 1789, and rose growers at once began to increase its size and fragrance by skillful selective breeding. By 1809 they had produced the sweet-smelling and voluminously petaled Rosa Indica Fragrans at right.

Here again Darwin was bringing his mind to bear on facts that everyone else was ignoring. It was no secret that breeders had produced new, improved varieties of cattle, chickens, dogs, pigeons, and vegetables. Yet these well-known changes had not dented the creationists' belief that species never changed by themselves. As far as they could see, such changes had been produced solely by man's efforts and therefore they were quite unnatural. What, they asked, did the work of stockbreeders have to do with the study of nature? Nothing, except that Darwin thought he ought to find out for himself how breeders went about their work of creating new varieties of living things.

The stockbreeders' method, he saw at once, was simple enough in principle. A breeder, then as now, looked for just those small, hereditary variations that Darwin believed were so important for evolution. It might be a cow that gave slightly more milk or that endured cold weather better than the rest of the herd. The breeder then deliberately selected all the cattle possessing this desired variation and kept them apart from the normal cattle. These variant animals he bred among themselves. If the variation was a truly hereditary one, then some of the offspring of these selected cattle would inherit this favorable variation. From among these variant offspring he then selected those few that showed the same variation to an even greater degree than the other variants. He bred these few apart, too. By continuing this "selective breeding" for several generations, he could produce a new variety of cattle, which had diverged considerably from its forebears in the particular characteristics that he wanted.

If something like the stockbreeder's selection operated in nature, thought Darwin, he would have a beautiful explanation of how species originated. By isolating the variants and breeding them apart, then selecting from the variants' offspring those that had the same variation to an even greater degree, a breeder could make a chance variation intensify over the generations. This was just what Darwin's theory required. "I soon perceived," Darwin said of his inquiries among the breeders, "that selection was the keystone of man's success in making useful races of animals and plants. But how selection could be applied to organisms living in the state of nature remained for some time a mystery to me." Actually, it was worse than a mystery. Far from acting as a watchful stockbreeder, nature's system of selection apparently weeded out precisely those variant offspring on which Darwin's whole theory depended.

It is the nature of genius, however, to be flexible of mind. Instead of nagging away at the puzzles that stumped him, Darwin took yet another line of attack.

His travels in South America had made him deeply interested in the mysterious extinction of species. His researches had constantly uncovered relics of vanished races of animals. Yet Darwin's observation of South American topography and rock formations had convinced him that Lyell was totally right in rejecting the theory of supernatural catastrophes, the accepted explanation for the sudden extinction of species. There had to be some other reason why species had disappeared in the past. After pondering this matter for some months, Darwin, early in 1838, came to a definite conclusion about the phenomenon of extinction. When he did, a light began to glow in the considerable darkness that surrounded him.

The answer, he believed, lay in Lyell's new geology itself. According to Lyell, the physical environment and climate had been slowly and gradually changing throughout the world. Europe, for example, had once been a tropical region but later grew so cold that it was covered with ice and snow. Therefore, Darwin reasoned, a species that had begun by being well adapted to its environment could easily have become less suited to it as that environment changed. Borrowing Lyell's idea, Darwin reasoned that these poorly adapted species might slowly lose out in the struggle for existence. In each generation slightly fewer members of the species would survive to maturity, and as a result, fewer offspring would be born in the next generation. Therefore, when one saw a rare species, such as the *avestruz Petise*, one was actually seeing a living species that was gradually becoming extinct.

"With respect to extinction," he wrote confidently in his notebook, "we can easily see that a variety of ostrich *(Petise)* may not be well adapted, and thus perish out; or on the other hand, like Orpheus [a Galápagos bird], being favourable, many might be produced . . . death of species is a consequence . . . of non-adaptation of circumstances." The environment changed, but the species did not. This was its doom, Darwin concluded. "They die, without [unless] they change."

It was several months before Darwin saw the astonishing significance of this conclusion. He saw that every naturalist, himself included, had been assuming as true what was indisputably false. On this false foundation Lyell had built his argument to prove that species cannot change. On

Appalled by the ruthlessness of the evolutionary process, the poet Tenny-son called nature "red in tooth and claw." As Darwin realized, the strug-gle for existence is fiercest within each species. Here, a dog fox (rear) snarls at a stronger rival who is entering his territory to challenge him.

this same false foundation creationists had erected their whole thesis. There was only one reason, Darwin realized, why Lyell could say that variant offspring had to be killed off in the struggle for existence. This reason was simply the belief that each individual species—as God's handiwork—was perfectly adapted to its environment. As a consequence, any change would of necessity be a change for the worse. But was this grand and fundamental assumption true? Darwin's explanation of extinction suggested, at least, that it could not *always* be true.

In the past, when the environment changed, some species adapted so poorly to the fresh conditions that they died out. Yet the environment is always changing. This was the whole point of Lyell's great work in geology, and by September, 1838, Darwin knew what it signified. Since the environment was always changing, no species could remain in a state of perfect adaptation to its environment.

Here was a truly radical thought, and it can be expressed very simply: *Every species has room for improvement.*

This meant, Darwin now saw, that every variant offspring was not necessarily inferior to its parents and would not necessarily be weeded out in the struggle for existence. It might even happen on occasion that the variant was slightly better adapted to the changing environment than its parents had been. In that case the struggle for existence might kill off the normal children, or those with useless kinds of variations, while the offspring with the favorable variation continued to flourish. The struggle for existence could "select" the variant instead of killing it off. As Darwin expressed it in his notebook: "All this agrees well with my view of those forms slightly favoured getting the upper hand and forming species."

Toward the end of September, 1838, Darwin stood on the very brink of his discovery. His ideas were still somewhat vague and sketchy in his mind. The occasional survival of a few slightly varying offspring did not really account for the vast changes that his theory of evolution required. Besides, the idea of certain variants "getting the upper hand," as he expressed it, was scarcely appropriate to a scientific theory.

On September 28, his mind saturated with ideas on the struggle for existence, Darwin sat down to read for amusement a book that had nothing to do with the study of nature. Before he finished the book, he was able to see with electrifying clarity just how badly adapted every species was and just how relentless was the struggle for survival.

A Guide To Earth History: CHATTO & WINDUS, LTD.

Maurice Wilson's rendering shows the dense tropical forest that covered Europe during the Carboniferous period, 300 million years ago. This lush woodland gradually fossilized into the beds of coal that provided power for the steam-driven machines of Victorian England's industrial revolution.

The book was entitled *An Essay on the Principles of Population*. It had been written in 1798 by a pessimistic English schoolmaster named Thomas Robert Malthus. Malthus tried to prove, by an ingenious mathematical argument, that it was impossible to improve the living conditions of mankind. Darwin had no interest in Malthus' social philosophy, but he was struck by the author's reasoning.

The world's supply of food, Malthus wrote, could increase only a little at a time, but the human population increased in "geometrical ratio." (This is the operation familiar to all when a number is doubled and redoubled. In a very small number of doublings, an extremely large number will be reached.) If every human couple, for example, gave birth to four children, Malthus said, the human population of the earth would double within one generation. If all the children reached maturity, married, and gave birth to four more children who also reached maturity, married, and had four children, then in a mere ten generations (about two hundred years) the world's population would have increased 512 times! In the eleventh generation it would have increased 1,024 times; by the twelfth, 2,048 times. What prevented this horrendous overpopulation, said Malthus, was the brutal and necessary fact that war, starvation, and disease killed off most people before they had a chance to have children at all.

Here, Darwin saw, was an extraordinary new way to measure the struggle for existence among all living things. Compared to man, other species have the capacity to reproduce their own kind at truly stupendous speeds. A single oyster can produce more than sixty million eggs in one season. Even creatures with far slower rates of reproduction have the power to choke the earth's surface with their offspring. The female elephant, as Darwin later calculated, lives one hundred years and normally gives birth in that time to just six children. Nevertheless, if each of these six children were to give birth to six more children, each of whom in turn gave birth to six children, in 750 years a single elephant pair could produce nineteen million descendants. Potentially at least, every living thing has this power to clog the world with its children in a very short time. This is true provided that a species meets one simple condition: that all its children live to maturity and produce children who in turn all live to maturity and produce more children.

But this condition is never met in nature. Billions upon billions of plant seeds are scattered on the wind each year and never take root. Billions of animal eggs are eaten or

This fight between two stags, whose horns have interlocked, could be for dominance over a herd, a territory, or even a single doe. It is part of the ceaseless competition between rival members of the same species for nature's severely limited means of subsistence.

Methods of reproduction employed by the dandelion and the squid make it clear how lavishly some species propagate themselves. At left, a dandelion parachutes its countless tiny seeds into the air to fall where they may. At right, transparent sacs of squid eggs, anchored to a rock, wave like an underwater flower at the mercy of the waves and currents.

destroyed or fail to be fertilized. The vast and overwhelming majority of seeds and eggs never produce a living thing. Countless numbers of plant sprouts and animal infants are killed off before they reach maturity—before they have a chance to reproduce. In the struggle for existence, most living things fail. We look out, Darwin said, and think we see the contented face of nature, while every second of every day a merciless and relentless slaughter is going on.

Here is the true picture of the struggle for survival. It is not merely the fixed battles between one species and its particular enemy, between the lion and the antelope, for example, or between the cobra and the mongoose. Such strife is an important part of the struggle, but the most intense struggle, as Darwin saw, is the ruthless competition between members of the same species for the food, water, light, warmth, and safety that each requires in order to survive. It is a competition so intense that only relatively few members of any species in any generation can emerge as the winners.

"It at once struck me," said Darwin, recalling his reading of Malthus on those momentous autumn days, "that under these circumstances favourable variations would tend to be preserved, and unfavourable ones to be destroyed. The result would be the formation of new species." The slightest chance variation that helps a particular member of a species to survive, Darwin saw, will give it a tiny advantage over its competitors. Such a lucky variant will be more likely than other members of the species to reach maturity and so give birth to children. The children who inherit this favorable variation will also tend to survive in greater numbers, proportionately, than the others. In time only the variants will have survived, while those members of the species that do not possess that favorable variation will have died out.

The competition, however, remains intense, so that even among these lucky variants, those that develop other favorable variations will also be favored in the struggle for existence. Over hundreds of thousands of generations the distant descendants of the original species will acquire so many favorable variations that they will constitute a new species. What is more, they will constitute a species that is ideally adapted to its environment, since it is precisely those variations that are useful for survival that are preserved in the relentless competition.

Darwin could now understand how a species could change. He could also see the enormous pressure that drove every species to change and to go on changing more and more, and in the process to keep producing living species. His haunting problems were solved. He held something that looked very much like the key to the origin of species, and he called it natural selection. "At last," wrote Darwin, "I had a theory to work with."

The French artist Gustave Doré depicted a Malthusian vision of overcrowding in "vile, smoky London," as Darwin sourly called it. The city's transition from a rural to an industrial center is dramatized by the smoky sky beyond the soaring dome of St. Paul's, while the streets are jammed with horse-drawn omnibuses (left foreground), flocks of sheep (in front of the railway bridge), and even a hearse (center).

THE YEARS AT DOWN

Between the day when Darwin discovered the key to the origin of species and the day on which he announced it to the world, twenty-one years were to go by. In any one week of the *Beagle* voyage he had had more adventures than he would experience in all those years combined. In his great fifteen-month period of intensive thought and research following the voyage, he had made more fundamental discoveries than he would make in all the quiet years to come. These twenty-one years, from 1838 to 1859, might truly be called Darwin's interlude of silence.

The chief outward events of this period are few but vitally important in Darwin's life. In January, 1839, he married. Almost immediately thereafter he began to suffer from mysterious and increasingly serious bouts of sickness. And in September, 1842, he moved with his growing family to the quiet country house in Kent where he was to spend the rest of his days.

Darwin had done much soul-searching on the subject of marriage before he proposed to Emma Wedgwood, the youngest of Uncle Jos' large family at Maer, although he had known and liked her since they both were children. Some notes still exist, scribbled sometime in 1837–38, in which he set down the arguments for and against marriage. As a bachelor, he would be free to work without interruption and without fear of poverty, to travel, and to enjoy the "conversation of clever men at clubs." But a married man had the pleasures of children and the constant companionship of "a nice soft wife on a sofa with good fire, and books and music perhaps." After comparing "this vision with the dingy reality of Grt Marlboro' St.," the notes triumphantly solve the theorem: "Marry—Marry—Marry. Q.E.D."

"A good, very ugly house with 18 acres," wrote Darwin in 1843 of his new house at Down. Today the house, seen from the lovely garden the Darwins laid out, still has the tranquil calm that led them to make it their home.

Fortunately for Darwin, Emma was the ideal wife. An attractive, strong-minded woman, a few months older than he, she took pleasure in caring for him and providing him with a serene and happy home. She also brought him a generous dowry and a regular annual income to add to the £13,000 provided by Dr. Darwin, so that the young couple were able to start married life with two maids, a cook, and a butler. They rented a furnished house in Upper Gower Street, which Charles christened "Macaw Cottage" because of its garishly colored wallpaper and drapes, and at once began entertaining their friends and relations.

The young husband was a busy man. He was working as hard as he could on a full-length book outlining his theory of how coral reefs were formed. At the same time, he was continuing the organization and editing of the zoological discoveries he had made while on the *Beagle*. In addition, he had accepted the time-consuming post of secretary of the Geological Society, which meant he had to attend regular meetings, as well as prepare and read his own papers to the society. In any moments he could spare, he went on reading and making notes on the origin of species, slipping the relevant papers into large portfolios under specific headings so that he could find them easily when he started to work on his great subject once more.

His first child, William, was born in December, 1839, to be followed two years later by a daughter, Annie, who was to become her father's favorite. Darwin took great pleasure in all his children, both as a father and as a scientist, making painstaking notes of his observations about their infant reactions and emotions. But his illness and exhaustion grew worse, and Emma found herself nursing him almost as constantly as she cared for their babies. A few hours of work would so tire him that he had to lie down and rest for the remainder of the day. An evening spent chatting with scientific friends would often leave him unfit for work the next morning. His illness took the form of mysterious headaches and stomach cramps, agonizing sleepless nights, and long spells of deep fatigue. He consulted one doctor after another, but although each diagnosed it afresh, no one could find a cure.

In 1841 Darwin thankfully gave up the secretaryship of the Geological Society, and he and Emma began looking for a house not too far from London where Charles could rest in rural quiet and seclusion. The following year the volume on coral reefs was finally completed and sent to press, and that September the Darwins moved to the country. Down House, in Kent, was reasonably priced, and although it was within sixteen miles of London Bridge, it was quiet, the chief requirement for both Emma and Charles.

Darwin at first announced his intention of visiting London every fortnight or three weeks "to keep up my communication with scientific men," but he found the two-hour journey more and more exhausting, and after a few years gave it up completely. Friends and relations came to visit him as often as they could and when he was well enough. But as his health grew worse and worse, Darwin seldom left Down and kept in touch with his family and his scientific friends mostly by letters. Hoping to gain some relief through a regular routine, Darwin tried to make each day at Down House as exactly like the day before as possible. Except for his wife and children and his correspondence, he was almost totally cut off from the world. The young voyager who only shortly before had endured five years of hardship and danger had become a semi-invalid.

In 1839 Darwin was made a Fellow of the Royal Society, England's oldest scientific organization, seen below in one of its regular meetings. The mace on the table at center was presented in 1663 by Charles II, a founding member. The right to put F.R.S. after his name is still an English scientist's badge of distinction.

Yet there is something truly dramatic about Darwin's years of silence, for behind his mysterious illness loomed his theory of evolution itself. Although he had suffered spells of sickness on the voyage of the *Beagle*, it was not until his return, during the very months when he had searched so successfully for the explanation of evolution, that serious illness first seized him. The stronger the theory of evolution by natural selection grew in Darwin's mind, the weaker and more unreliable his body became. "I am grown a dull, old spiritless dog to what I used to be," he wrote sadly to his cousin William Fox, as if he were prematurely aged at thirty-one. To Lyell he confided, "It is a bitter mortification to me to digest the conclusion that 'the race is for the strong' and that I shall probably do little but be content to admire the strides others make in science." Instead of

"He is the most transparent man I ever saw," said Emma Wedgwood of the cousin she was to marry. Water colors painted in 1840 by the popular portraitist George Richmond show how alike Emma and Charles were in looks. Their similarity in temperament made their marriage a most happy one.

feeling a surge of pride and happiness as he grasped one of the greatest of scientific truths, Darwin was conscious only of feeling sickly, weak, and nerve-racked.

Why this should be so is impossible to say for sure. Some historians have theorized that Darwin was neurotically obsessed by his overdominant father and that his lack of confidence in his ability to measure up to his father's standards was reflected in chronic invalidism. Others believe that he was a genuine hypochondriac and that his wife's devotion and patience as a nurse made being ill almost a pleasure. Most recently the suggestion has been made that during his South American travels he contracted Chagas' disease, a chronic tropical infection that penetrates the bloodstream and affects the heart. Over a period of years, Chagas' disease produces almost all the symptoms that afflicted Darwin, and he recorded in his journal that, while in Chile, he was bitten by the particular bug, the Benchuca, that we now know transmits the infection. ·

Whatever the reason for his ill health, Darwin was to spend the years from 1842 to 1846 dutifully working on more books about his geological observations made during the *Beagle*'s voyage. In 1842, immediately after he had sent his book on coral reefs to press, he allowed himself the satisfaction of writing down a brief, thirty-five page abstract of "my theory" in pencil. Two years later he enlarged this into a full, 230-page outline that crystallized many of his ideas about the origin of species. Obviously, he was hoping to get down to serious work on his beloved project, but he was deflected instead into a study of barnacles.

He had intended simply to write a brief monograph on the subject of an interesting barnacle found off the Chilean coast. His investigations broadened, however, until he found himself making an exhaustive analysis of every order of barnacles known to man. Working patiently, he ultimately dissected and analyzed some ten thousand separate barnacles. It took him eight years, and barnacles became such a feature of the household that one of his sons, visiting at a neighboring house, innocently asked his friends where their father kept his barnacles. It was not until September, 1854, that Darwin completed his study and sent every barnacle away from Down. He had spent the incredible total of eight full years in this scholarly drudgery. "I doubt," he later confessed a little guiltily, "whether the work was worth the consumption of so much time." Perhaps it was not, but it had helped him to put off a little longer the dreaded day when he had to present his ideas on evolution to the world.

Added to Darwin's physical isolation at Down House was his sense of intellectual isolation from fellow scientists. The theory of evolution, he feared, cut him off from the respectable world of science. Here he was, a modest and unassuming young man who now held a theory that most people despised and few people would even listen to with respect. To admit to a belief that species change, said Darwin, "is like confessing to a murder." To propose a theory of evolution to the public was to bring a storm down upon one's head.

It is hard to convey the combination of disgust and horrified interest that the idea of evolution then inspired. In 1844, for example, a man named Robert Chambers published a book called *Vestiges of the Natural History of Creation*.

These engravings illustrate work on which Darwin labored from 1838 to 1854 in moments of good health that became increasingly rare. The chart expounds his theory that coral reefs are of two kinds by coloring blue atolls and barrier reefs in areas where the earth has subsided and using pink for fringing reefs around upthrust volcanoes (stars). The colorful barnacles at left are varieties of the Balanus family, which are found all over the world attached by disks to rocks in shallow water.

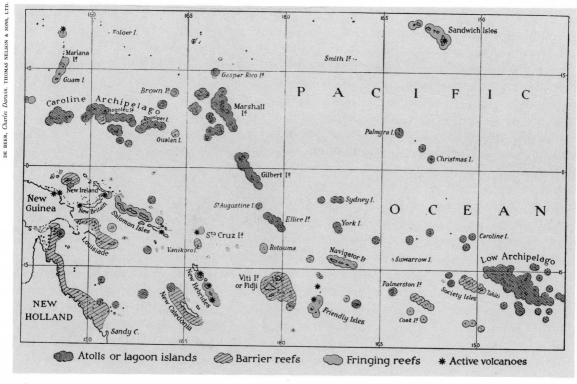

In it the author, who was an editor and book publisher by trade, revived the old Lamarckian idea of "lower" animals evolving by an inner law into "higher types" of animals. The *Vestiges* was full of all the vague, unsound ideas that Darwin had been at such pains to avoid, but it proclaimed evolution and so it created a major scandal in England. The author knew it would, so he prudently published the book anonymously. For months during 1844 the favorite London game was trying to guess "Mr. Vestiges'" identity. Some people even suggested that the secret author was Queen Victoria's twenty-five-year-old husband, Prince Albert. In some circles the name of Darwin was mentioned, a fact that gave Darwin himself no pleasure at all. Such illustrious scientists as Charles Lyell demolished the *Vestiges* in print— an easy task, considering what a jumble of ideas it contained.

The noted geologist Adam Sedgwick went one step further to satisfy the public's sense of outrage. He likened the anonymous author to the serpent in the Garden of Eden, a reptile who would poison the minds of "our glorious matrons and maids" by teaching them "that they are the children of apes and the breeders of monsters." The book, said Sedgwick, rising to a high pitch of denunciation, was "rank, unbending and degrading materialism." So much for the battered *Vestiges of the Natural History of Creation*, which nevertheless went through ten editions in as many years. Then, as now, notoriety helped to sell a book.

Darwin was left with no illusions that his own work would get a fair trial. Fearing that his cherished theory might one day be trampled and crushed like the *Vestiges* and so in the end come to nothing, he determined to buttress it with all the examples and proofs that he could muster. All he dared hope, he said, was that one competent person might someday accept the truth of his theory. Yet here, precisely, was where the trouble lay. Darwin could not find that one person. At the very mention of the idea that species change, even a close friend like Lyell turned a deaf ear. For a while, Darwin sought endorsement from another scientific friend, Joseph Dalton Hooker. Here, too, his hopes were dashed.

Joseph Hooker, a young and extremely brilliant botanist, had first met Darwin in the summer of 1839, just before he himself set sail on a three-year voyage aboard the *Erebus*, a British survey vessel making the first attempt to locate the southern magnetic pole. Hooker, a friend of the Lyell family, had read Darwin's account of the *Beagle* voyage, and when he returned from his Antarctic expedition in

Richmond's sketch of Darwin's confidant and friend Joseph Dalton Hooker was made in 1855 when the botanist was thirty-eight.

1842, he and Darwin instantly developed a warm, working friendship that was to last the rest of their lives. Few weeks went by without their exchanging letters, and when Darwin's health was at its worst, Hooker was almost the only person who still continued to visit him at Down House. Darwin applied to Hooker for botanical information and personal advice and encouragement. Yet, although the young botanist read the 1842 and 1844 outlines of Darwin's theory and agreed with some of his conclusions, even he could not accept the idea that species could change.

Other scientists were less sympathetic. Once, in 1846, when he cautiously revealed to a zoologist colleague that he had come to believe that "species are mutable [capable of change]," the friend, who was also a clergyman, wrote back demanding how Darwin could dare to think his ideas proved truths.

The words of Darwin's modest reply were tinged with sadness.

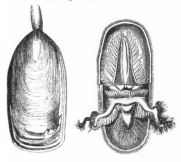

Vestiges' *author, Robert Chambers, used this extremely simple bivalve shell from the Silurian period, 440 million years ago, to illustrate his theory that primitive forms of life have a tendency to evolve in an upward direction.*

I must have expressed myself with singular inaccuracy if I led you to suppose that I meant to say that my conclusions were inevitable. They have become so, after years of weighing puzzles, to myself *alone*; but in my wildest day-dreams, I never expect more than to be able to show that there are two sides to the question of the immutability of species. . . . A long searching amongst agricultural and horticultural books and people makes me believe (I well know how absurdly presumptuous this must appear) that I see the way in which new varieties become exquisitely adapted to the external conditions of life and to other surrounding beings. I am a bold man to lay myself open to being thought a complete fool, and a most deliberate one. . . . Pray do not think that I am so blind as not see that there are numerous immense difficulties in my notions.

Once the barnacles were out of the way, Darwin began, whenever he was well enough, to cope systematically with these "numerous immense difficulties." His correspondence, and the experiments that he carried out at Down, covered a remarkable variety of subjects. When he was studying practical variation in species, his cousin William Fox was pressed into service to procure young pigeons. Should an old hen, he wrote to Fox, "die or become so old as to be *useless*, I wish you would send her to me per rail, addressed to 'C. Darwin, care of Mr. Acton, Post-office, Bromley, Kent.'"

Through Fox, Darwin also offered rewards of one shilling for every half-dozen lizard eggs brought in by local schoolboys, adding that "if snake's eggs were brought in

LEECH, *Young Troublesome*, 1850: NEW YORK PUBLIC LIBRARY

Life in large Victorian families was not always as strict as is thought. The seven young Darwins who filled Down House with noise and laughter no doubt slid down banisters like this octet, portrayed by caricaturist John Leech. Unlike their outraged father at left, however, Darwin was never reproving, and one child even offered him a bribe of sixpence to leave his work and join in their games.

mistake it would be very well, for I want such also.'' He was carrying out a long series of experiments in which he tried to show that eggs and seeds could be transported to remote islands by floating on the sea. This was an hypothesis that Hooker strongly insisted was impossible, although he obligingly furnished Darwin with seeds and statistics from the Royal Botanical Gardens at Kew, where he became Assistant Director in 1855. To prove Hooker wrong, Darwin first put seeds in buckets of salt water to see if they could survive a long soaking, then fed them to birds to see if they would germinate after they were voided. His children thought salting seeds was a fine competitive game. They "asked me often whether I should beat Dr. Hooker," Darwin reported. (He did.)

Apart from these simple distractions, the years at Down House went by slowly and uneventfully, just as Darwin wished them to do. With his own private income and that of his wife, he was financially secure, and in fact, quite prosperous, although he always lived economically. He wanted little from the world and the world demanded little from him. He had a fine reputation among scientists, however, and one of them, the able and extremely ambitious young zoologist Thomas Henry Huxley, told a friend in 1851 that Darwin "might be anything if he had good health." But the constant weakness continued, and Darwin adapted his whole routine to it. "My life goes on like clockwork," he wrote to his old friend Captain Fitzroy, "and I am fixed on the spot where I shall end it." At Down House, for forty years Darwin was to live, as he himself put it, "the life of a hermit."

He was not quite a hermit, for Down House rang with the laughter of children, and often enough, with the clear, easy laugh of Darwin himself. In spite of ill health, Darwin's life, said his son Francis, was one of "quiet gladness," and the "good, very ugly house" he had chosen as his retreat was a happy and even idyllic place. Almost every other year there was a new addition to the growing Darwin family until, by 1851, the plain white house contained seven Darwin children, five sons and two daughters. All of them believed, to the end of their lives, that they had grown up at Down in a kind of earthly paradise. There, overlooking the chalk hills and leafy hedgerows of Kent, far away from crowds and complications, the Darwins lived in a little world of their own where nobody spoke an angry word and where everyone was free to do as he pleased.

There was hardly a home like it in all England, for Darwin's way of bringing up his children was exactly the reverse of the strict and rulebound upbringing normally practiced in those days. At Down the Darwin children were free to ramble all over the house and gardens and often enough into their father's own study. His daughter always remembered his patient look when he said once, "Don't you think you could not come in again? I have been interrupted very often." As a father, Darwin was infinitely affectionate, sympathetic, and indulgent. Once he walked into the living room to find his little son Leonard jumping up and down on the sofa, which was strictly forbidden. "Oh, Lenny, Lenny," said Darwin sadly, "that's

Although he could have afforded expensive scientific equipment, Darwin preferred simple, often makeshift tools for his experiments. This microscope is one of his few totally precise instruments.

against all rules." To which young Leonard replied, "Then I think you had better go out of the room."

Darwin found it impossible to play the role of the stern, Victorian father. Instead, he treated his children as his equals and took part in their doings as if he were a fellow child and not the master of the house. He loved them all intensely and they were one of the great pleasures of his quiet life. "When you were very young," he noted in the *Recollections* he wrote for them when he was an old and famous man, "it was my greatest delight to play with you all, and I think with a sigh that such days can never return." The death of his ten-year-old daughter Annie in 1851 was the greatest grief in his long life. Twenty-five years later the thought of her could still move him to tears.

Each day at Down House, Darwin followed the same unvarying routine. After an early breakfast—and often enough, a sleepless night—he would do a brief stint of work from eight to nine-thirty. Then for an hour he would lie down on the sofa while his wife read a popular novel aloud to him. Almost any novel would do, he said, as long as the heroine was pretty and the story had a happy ending. From ten-thirty to twelve he would do some more work, and that usually completed the day's labors. Little as it was, Darwin was happy to do that much. On especially energetic days he would announce, to the family's amuse-

*Despite Emma's care, Darwin's invalidism increased. A daguerreotype (left) of him
with his eldest son, William, taken around 1843, shows a shocking change from the
portrait on page 89. Each evening at Down he would rest on the sofa in the living
room (above) while Emma, an excellent pianist, soothed him with music he loved.*

ment, "I've done a good day's work." After that, he would take his midday stroll around "The Sand-Walk," a gravel path around a strip of meadow, which was lined with shade trees. On these walks he would stride vigorously along, swinging his walking stick, carefully recording with pieces of flint the number of turns he had taken. But by the time he returned to the house, his step would have lost its spring. His frail body could not long sustain any exertion.

After lunch he would read the paper and answer his mail until three o'clock. Then, after another rest, he would come downstairs at exactly four o'clock to take his afternoon walk. On this stroll he would examine the various plant experiments that he was conducting as part of his research on evolution. At such times, his son Francis recalled, he would talk about the plants as if they were people and about the experiments as if they were amusing games. "The little beggars are doing just what I don't want them to," he would say when an experiment went wrong.

After this tour, Darwin would have a light supper and then perhaps play a little backgammon with Emma or listen to her playing the piano before going to bed early. Except for his rare journeys to see relatives or the infrequent visits of scientific friends, the routine never changed, not even on Sundays.

As methodical in keeping check on his health as he was in tending his experiments, Darwin noted daily how he felt in the daytime and how he slept during the night. This September, 1851, chart records weeks of better health than usual, although many entries of "Well, very" on the day side deteriorate into "moderate" or "indifferent" in the night column.

On many occasions, however, Darwin went away to private clinics to undergo what was known as "the water-cure." This consisted essentially of a series of daily baths, with the patient wrapped up in wet sheets. The water-cure never cured Darwin and he wondered at times whether the doctor who recommended it was a quack. But the baths did make him feel better, largely because they took his mind off evolution. "At last I fell asleep on the grass," he once reported to his wife from a water-cure establishment near Farnham in Surrey, "and awoke with a chorus of birds singing around me, and squirrels running up the trees, and some woodpeckers laughing, and it was as pleasant and rural a scene as ever I saw, and I did not care one penny how any of the beasts or birds had been formed."

Not caring must have been a welcome relief to Darwin, for although he lived like a semi-invalid, he was ruled by a powerful passion: his iron determination to make his theory of evolution as invulnerable as he possibly could. Over the long years of silence, Darwin bent the whole force of his genius to anticipating in advance every argument that science might devise against his ideas. Whenever he came upon a fact that did not fit his theory, he carefully wrote it down to make sure he did not overlook it. Until he had anticipated every argument and worked out an unbeatable answer, he would not publish his theory.

Over the passing years, he had to grapple, for example, with the sudden appearance of fresh species in fossils taken from rock strata of different periods. As Darwin himself admitted, if this fossil record were a true account of the history of life, "my theory must be smashed." It will soon be seen how brilliantly Darwin dealt with this problem when he came to write his remarkable book *The Origin of Species*. Too numerous to list are the other "difficulties," as Darwin called them, which he thought up for himself—and solved —in the isolation of Down House.

By Darwin's theory of evolution by natural selection, every change in a species was one that had contributed to that species' survival. Therefore, if scientists could point out one single feature of any living thing that could not help it to survive, the theory of evolution would be seriously weakened.

One problem he had to face was that of how the eye had evolved in the course of evolutionary history. The difficulty here was this: A perfect, working eye is obviously useful in helping an animal to survive. Yet, according to the theory of evolution, there must once have been a time when no

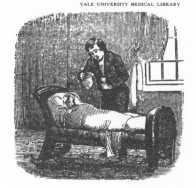

When taking the water cure, Darwin endured this treatment—wet sheet packing—in which the patient lies completely swaddled in clammy sheets for an hour or more. This 1849 engraving from a New York water-cure journal shows that hydropathy was as popular in America as it was in Europe.

animal species had yet evolved an eye that could see. An imperfect eye, a vestige that has only just begun to evolve into an eye, would seem to be totally useless, for what good is an eye that does not permit its owner to see? But if an imperfectly evolved eye is useless, then it will not be preserved by natural selection. Also, it is impossible for it to improve gradually, since a small improvement would not be enough to make it work perfectly—and if it does not work, it is useless, and hence the improvement will not be preserved. Therefore, it would seem, the eye is one organ that could not possibly have evolved. In *The Origin of Species* Darwin was to offer a neat solution to this question.

There were more, many more, such puzzles, and Darwin spent sleepless nights grappling with newly discovered difficulties or some stubborn facts that threatened to explode his theory "like an empty puff-ball."

In 1856, fourteen years after moving to Down and eighteen years after he had discovered the principle of natural selection, Darwin at last decided to write down his theory for publication. He did so reluctantly, at the urging of both Lyell and Hooker. The two scientists could not as yet believe in Darwin's theory themselves, but as his friends they felt he should offer the fruits of so much hard work to the world. Lyell, in particular, warned him that unless he published his theory at least in outline, somebody else might publish before he did and establish a priority he would find hard to overcome. Darwin, however, disagreed strongly. The idea of publishing his theory without a mass of supporting facts gave him, he said, "the wibber-jibbers."

Instead of writing a sketch, Darwin sat down in May, 1856, to compile a huge and weighty account of his theory, under the tentative title of "Natural Selection." It was to be a monumental book of well over a thousand pages, stuffed with the mass of facts that he had gathered so laboriously over the years to protect his unpopular theory from the scientific wolves. He had no desire whatever to make his book easy to read. For twenty months he worked in leisurely fashion on his "species book," as if he had all the time in the world. Hugh Falconer, a fellow scientist, warned him bluntly that "you will do more mischief than any ten other naturalists would do good," but Darwin was undismayed and the work went along quite smoothly.

Then, on June 18, 1858, a letter arrived at Down House. It was from Alfred Russel Wallace, a thirty-five-year-old English naturalist who was exploring the East Indies. Wallace had already been in correspondence with Darwin briefly.

While experimenting on natural selection, Darwin raised pigeons in order to study their development. Two engravings that still hang at Down show the sharp differentiation between the carrier pigeon (top) and the puffed-up pouter pigeon (below), which both evolved from the same ancestor.

Enclosed in the letter was an essay that he had just written, one that he hoped Darwin might find interesting. Darwin read it and found it a great deal more than interesting. It gave him the shock of his life, for the essay contained, point by point, his own entire theory of evolution by natural selection!

"I never saw a more striking coincidence," Darwin wrote that day to Lyell, "If Wallace had my manuscript sketch written out in 1842, he could not have made a better short abstract!" It was truly a striking coincidence, one of the most remarkable cases known of two researchers working independently and coming to exactly the same conclusion.

Darwin was dreadfully distressed. His first reaction was to publish Wallace's paper and abandon his own claim to priority; then, as he thought it over, he could not bear the prospect of totally relinquishing his rights over material he had been sifting and shaping for twenty grueling years. He wrote again to Lyell and to Hooker, begging for advice.

They acted promptly, presenting both Wallace's essay and Darwin's 1844 outline of his theory at a meeting of the Linnean Society, so that both men shared in the credit but Darwin's priority was clearly established. With almost saintly generosity, Wallace subsequently refused to take any credit away from Darwin. As he said, Darwin had discovered the theory of evolution by natural selection many years before he had and had overcome theoretical difficulties in establishing it that Wallace himself had not even begun to think out.

To reinforce his prior claim, however, Darwin had to stop perfecting his mammoth work, and on July 20, 1859, he began the "brief abstract" that was to become famous as *The Origin of Species*. After so many years of weighing puzzles, it took him only eight months to write the book that formulated his entire theory. By March, 1859, the manuscript was complete, and Lyell's own publisher, John Murray, accepted it on very generous terms.

After much rewriting and correction, the final publisher's proofs were dispatched in September. At last, Darwin's theory of evolution—the joy and burden of his life—was off his mind and into print. The single volume, bound in plain green cloth, came out in November, 1859, and sold for the price of fifteen shillings. The great men of science would soon find out that this particular work on evolution was a great deal more formidable than *Vestiges of the Natural History of Creation*. Darwin had seen to that.

Alfred Russel Wallace, the self-taught naturalist who independently chanced on Darwin's exact theories concerning the origin of species, is seen in an 1853 picture.

VI

THE ORIGIN OF SPECIES

The basic principles of Darwin's theory of evolution can be outlined in perhaps a dozen sentences. *The Origin of Species*, however, is five hundred pages long, and as Darwin himself exclaimed when he reread it: "Oh! my gracious, it is tough reading." The reason for this is that he had to do more than merely outline his theory: he had to persuade other men that it was true. *The Origin of Species* is, therefore, one long, relentless argument in support of the theory of evolution by natural selection. Its purpose was to make men accept a theory that they did not wish to accept.

Carrying out this purpose was an extremely difficult task. Indeed, Alfred Russel Wallace admitted that he himself could not have done it. It must be remembered that Darwin could not demonstrate evolution by some simple experiment or observation, for evolution cannot be seen by any observer. On the contrary, direct observation shows that species do not seem to change at all. Nor could Darwin display to skeptics a long row of fossils illustrating the slow, gradual changes undergone by a particular species. He had no such row of fossils to show. What then could he do? He could demonstrate that his explanation of the origin of species was far superior to any other explanation that science could offer—and this was exactly what he did.

Darwin divides his long argument into three distinct parts. In the first part he shows that natural selection is a reality that can produce vast changes in living things. In the second part, he shows that his theory cannot be contradicted by any known facts or arguments. In the last part, Darwin demonstrates his theory's power to explain the most diverse and fundamental facts of biology better than they have ever been explained before. This is the most crucial part of his argument, for in science the best theory is the one that offers the most satisfactory and complete explanations. By the sheer weight of this army of explained facts Darwin hoped to overwhelm the enemies of evolution.

BAKER, *Calico Painting . . . in the East Indies*, 1921: NEW YORK PUBLIC LIBRARY

Darwin's evolutionary theory was to reinterpret the centuries-old picture of life as a tree with many branches displaying the various species. This eighteenth-century pattern not only perches birds and animals amid the branches and roots but also adds complexity by slightly varying each leaf.

His first step, then, is to show that the process he called natural selection truly operates in nature. As we have already seen, natural selection is the result of two fundamental principles: first, that small hereditary variations crop up at random in the offspring of all living things (a truth Darwin establishes in the second chapter of the *Origin*), and secondly, that there is a struggle for existence among living things. In Chapter Three of the book, Darwin shows that this struggle exists and that it profoundly affects the life of every living organism. As will be seen, it is Darwin's understanding of the struggle for existence and all its many consequences that gives his theory its strength.

Darwin's conception of the struggle for existence was based on the indisputable fact that living things reproduce

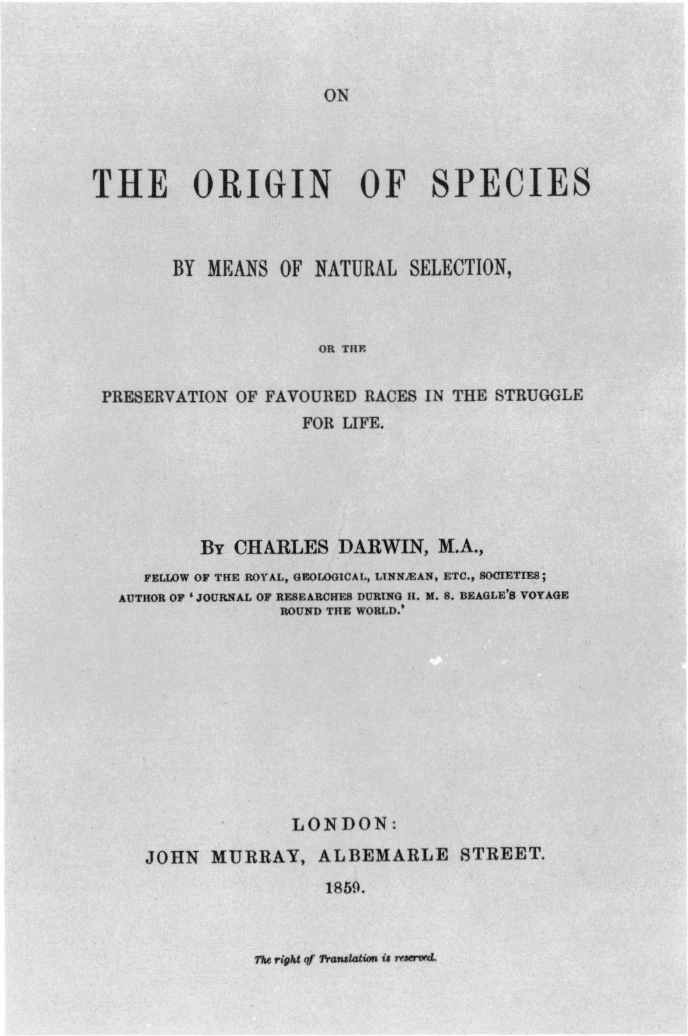

ON

THE ORIGIN OF SPECIES

BY MEANS OF NATURAL SELECTION,

OR THE

PRESERVATION OF FAVOURED RACES IN THE STRUGGLE FOR LIFE.

By CHARLES DARWIN, M.A.,

FELLOW OF THE ROYAL, GEOLOGICAL, LINNÆAN, ETC., SOCIETIES;
AUTHOR OF 'JOURNAL OF RESEARCHES DURING H. M. S. BEAGLE'S VOYAGE
ROUND THE WORLD.'

LONDON:
JOHN MURRAY, ALBEMARLE STREET.
1859.

The right of Translation is reserved.

Publisher John Murray telescoped Darwin's suggested title for his book, An Abstract of an Essay on the Origin of Species and Varieties Through Natural Selection, *into the still-lengthy title page at left. This first edition was sold out on publication day.*

their own kind in a geometrical ratio. "There is no exception to the rule," he writes, "that every organic being naturally increases at so high a rate that, if not destroyed, the earth would soon be covered by the progeny of a single pair." However, since there is no increase whatever in the means by which living things can survive, far more individuals are born than can possibly grow to maturity. This is the central principle of the struggle for existence.

One consequence of this brutal fact is that members of every species are forever striving to find more food, more space, and fresh means of survival for themselves. Long ago in Uruguay, Darwin remarks, he had seen woodpeckers—creatures, that is, that are beautifully adapted to forest life—living where hardly a tree could be found. This is a puzzling fact until we remember the struggle for existence. In their fight to survive, woodpeckers will move into any empty space where they can find fresh means of surviving, even if it means abandoning the forests, their natural home.

Such empty spaces, however, are far from plentiful. Because of the high birth rate of all living things, the world of nature, says Darwin, is an exceedingly crowded place. This crowding has serious and dramatic consequences. Should one species increase in number, some other species must decrease in number, for there is never room enough, or food enough, for more. This principle is fundamental to Darwin's whole theory, and every gardener learns it when he fails to uproot crabgrass from his lawn. This hardy invader will not merely flourish, it will flourish at the expense of the lawn grass and swiftly kill it off. The tender lawn grass and the tough crabgrass will not long exist side by side. They are rivals because they require the same scarce necessities of life, and in the struggle for existence, the stronger will always conquer its weaker rival.

Here, Darwin emphasizes yet another consequence of the struggle for existence: the most important force in the life of any living thing is the other living things among which it dwells. In the life of the lawn grass, for example, the existence of crabgrass is obviously a crucial factor, more important than the sunshine and rain that the lawn receives. This is true for all living things, says Darwin, although it has not previously been recognized. Naturalists, he says, have assumed that physical environment and climate play the key roles in the life of every species. They supposed, for example, that plants imported from other countries could never grow wild in England because the cold English climate would be fatal to them. But, in fact,

Darwin's genius for detailed observation emerges from the Origin's *discussion of slave-making ants, which war upon other ant colonies and carry off the enemies' pupa, or eggs, as this ant is doing. Once hatched, these captives obediently carry out all the work of the colony that enslaved them.*

NATIONAL AUDUBON SOCIETY: PHOTO, BERNARD L. GLUCK

Darwin points out, what keeps these plants from being domesticated in English gardens is not the climate but the competition from native English plants. These plants are better adapted to the climate than are the foreign ones and so they kill off the intruders in the struggle for existence.

Clearly, the life of one group of creatures will depend on the activities of some other group of creatures. These, in turn, will depend on yet other species, and so on and on. "A complex web of life," says Darwin, unites all the living things in a particular region into a surprisingly complicated system. The amount of red clover in any area, he points out, depends on the number of bumblebees available to spread the clover's pollen from flower to flower, thus causing fertilization. The number of bumblebees depends mainly on the number of field mice, for the field mice destroy the bees' nests and honeycombs. The number of field mice depends in turn on the number of cats, which prey upon the mice. This system is so nicely balanced that around rural villages where there are a large number of cats, there is also a large amount of red clover. The cats, by killing the mice, permit the survival of more bumblebees, which fertilize more clover and so increase the clover population. Cats are thus part of the environment in which red clover lives, as indeed are all the living things that affect the life of red clover in any way. It is an exceedingly complex environment and this is likewise true for all living things.

Such, in brief, is the struggle for existence and its fundamental consequences. This struggle, Darwin points out, "almost invariably will be most severe between the individuals of the same species, for they frequent the same districts, require the same food, and are exposed to the same dangers." With this telling remark, he is ready to demonstrate the reality of natural selection.

At this point, Darwin has established that small, hereditary variations crop up at random among the offspring of any species, and he has also shown that a struggle for existence pervades the life of every living thing. The deduction he makes from these two points is that there is a natural selection of favorable variations.

Darwin puts his argument into the form of a question: "Can we doubt (remembering that many more individuals are born than can possibly survive) that individuals bearing any advantage, however slight, over others, will have the best chance of surviving and of procreating their kind?" In other words, offspring inheriting a favorable variation are more likely to reach maturity than members of the same

One example of living things' interdependence is the bumblebee (above), which visits red clover fields (below) seeking nectar. Pollen rubbed off on the bee is carried to fertilize other blossoms, thus ensuring the clover's renewal.

species that lack this advantage. It may happen, perhaps, that fifteen per cent of the favored variants in any given generation will survive to produce their variant children, while only five per cent of the others will do so. After many, many generations, however, these slightly differing percentages will tell: the variants will increase in number while the non-variants will decrease. These favored variants in time will come to form a distinct variety of that species, slightly different from the parent species. This, in essence, is what natural selection means.

It frequently happens that other members of the same species will inherit a different kind of favorable variation and come to form yet another variety. But competition is usually most intense between members of the same species, which means that representatives of the parent species will find themselves struggling to survive against their own superior varieties. Being superior, the variants will kill off their own parent species. "Each new variety or species," writes Darwin, "during the progress of its formation will *generally* press hardest on its nearest kindred, and tend to exterminate them." In time, the parent species may even become extinct and be represented on earth solely by these few successful varieties.

These new improved varieties will usually become more and more unlike the original parent species. This is so, in general, because additional favorable variations will continue to crop up among the improved varieties. In the continuing struggle for existence, these new favored variants will beat out the "parent" variety just as that variety had beaten out its own parent species. After hundreds of thousands of generations, the successful surviving varieties will have become so distinct from the original parent species —now dead—that they will constitute a group of new species. They have sprung from the parent species like countless branches from a giant tree trunk.

These surviving new species, Darwin notes, will tend to look alike because they share many physical traits inherited from their common ancestor. They retain a family resemblance. This is a vital point, because naturalists had long recognized that certain species look strikingly alike. Such a group of similar-looking species is called a genus, a familiar example being the genus *Felis*, which includes the lion, the tiger, the leopard, the jaguar, and the household cat. Naturalists who believed in the separate creation of each species had never questioned why God should have made several species look so similar. Darwin's theory provides the simple,

Nature's relentless struggle is symbolized by the lizard swallowing a grasshopper (near left). To ensure their food supply, migrating geese (above) fly thousands of miles in autumn and spring. Taking refuge amid the tentacles of a sea anemone (far left) is a clown fish, the only fish immune to their paralyzing sting. Scientists are unsure what service the anemone receives in exchange.

decisive explanation: members of the same genus look alike because they are descended from a common ancestor.

Note, too, that natural selection does not depend on the chance appearance of large and strikingly useful variations. Even the most trifling advantage, as Darwin points out, will be preserved by natural selection. This is so, precisely because so very few members of any species survive to maturity. In these conditions only the very best survive, even if they are best by only the minutest degree.

Nor is natural selection limited to just a few obvious kinds of advantages, such as sharp teeth and claws, or thick fur for animals living in cold climates. As Darwin has shown, every creature lives in a "complex web of relationships" with the living things around it. Since success in the struggle for life will depend on thousands of different factors, it can be improved in a wide variety of ways. Any minute change in any part of any creature, therefore, may prove useful in that creature's particular battle for life. This is why Darwin's theory can explain, in general, the evolution of complex internal organs. Not only will the tiniest advantage be preserved by natural selection, but the kinds of favorable variations are unlimited. Evolution by natural selection is an efficient explanation of how species originate.

In the second part of *The Origin of Species*, Darwin raises a critical question: Can his theory be proved false by any known facts or arguments? Can anyone raise a serious objection to it that cannot be satisfactorily explained away? One by one, Darwin himself raises objections to his theory. Some are long-standing arguments against evolution; some of them he had thought of himself. One by one he overcomes them.

He first tackles the problem of the so-called transitional forms, which the theory of evolution supposedly cannot explain. According to creationists, if living things had gradually evolved from more ancient species, then there must have existed at one time "transitional" ancestors that looked almost like these living species. At some time in the past, for example, there must have existed near-horses and near-tigers. How is it that these are not alive today?

This was a good argument against Lamarck's theory, but not against Darwin's. As he had already demonstrated, the success of one species in the struggle for existence means the death of its inferior rival. "Thus extinction and natural selection go hand in hand," writes Darwin. "The parent and all the transitional varieties will generally have been exterminated by the very process of the formation and perfection of the new form." When the tiger evolved, in other words, it beat out the near-tiger and caused its extinction. This is why we do not see near-tigers or any other transitional forms alive today.

Another serious objection to the theory concerns the evolution of highly complex organs. Is it really possible to believe, Darwin asks, that natural selection could have produced the eye of the eagle? "[This] seems, I freely confess, absurd in the highest degree." Nor is this an easy objection to answer, for there exists no fossil record of the long series of steps by which the true seeing eye has evolved. Nevertheless, says Darwin, the difficulty can be overcome. When we look at living species, we notice that animals' ability to see varies greatly. It ranges, in a long, graded series with thousands of tiny steps, from the most rudimentary reaction to light to the highly complex mechanism of human vision. Certain lowly organisms, for example, possess only the ability to react to light. Somewhat more developed creatures can distinguish light from darkness. Some more advanced animals possess a true optic nerve, although they lack an eye at the end of it. In one such species, the optic nerve ends in a convex bulge. Here, says Darwin, we clearly have a primitive form of lens. Other species have slightly more perfected eyes. Noting these gradual steps, he says, we can well understand how the eye could have evolved through the preservation of small, favorable variations.

Here, Darwin neatly turns the tables on the creationists by asking how they would explain this marvelous gradation in the means of seeing. Since, by their theory, each species was created separately, why should God have created, for example, a species with an optic nerve ending in a useless bulge? On the other hand, if the eye had evolved over millions of years through the accumulation of small favorable variations, we should expect to see living things with eyes in all stages of development, as indeed we do.

Darwin then takes up an objection that his theory seems almost incapable of explaining. How can natural selection explain the origin of mammals that live in the water, such as whales and otters, or mammals that can fly, such as bats? By Darwin's theory, the ancestor of the otter must have been a land-dwelling animal, as most mammals are. How then could this ancestor enter the water before it became adapted to its water life?

In Darwin's answer to this question we can see the importance of his understanding of the struggle for existence. Every living thing, Darwin notes, will move into any new

The eye, Darwin reasoned, had gradually evolved from a rudimentary nerve to the complex mechanism used by a predatory species, such as this eagle owl, whose fierce, unblinking eye is complete with central pupil, outer iris, and delicately lashed protective lids.

place in nature if it can find fresh means of survival there. Woodpeckers live on the Uruguayan plains; web-footed ducks live hundreds of miles from water. Obviously, some mammal species may begin frequenting the shores of oceans and rivers if it aids them in their struggle to survive. When any animal changes its habits even slightly, it has drastically changed its living environment. An animal that begins to eat a different food will start facing a different battery of competitors. A fresh set of variations will thus become useful in its battle for survival. If a land-dwelling mammal starts frequenting river shores in order to feed upon fish, any variation that enables this creature to catch fish more efficiently will be preserved by natural selection. For example, it may well develop fur that is slightly more water-repellent. In time, this creature's descendants may form varieties well adapted for occasional diving into the river. In other words, it can become a water-dwelling animal by many slow stages.

Nor is this a merely theoretical answer. Darwin describes a species of polecat, which actually exists in North America, that is equally at home on land and in the water and divides its time between the two. In winter, this polecat preys upon land mice, but in summer it dives for fish. Unlike other species of polecats, it has short legs, webbed feet, smooth fur, and an otterlike tail, all features that are useful for swimming. If spending more time in the water became necessary in its struggle for survival, then any variations that enabled it to do so would be preserved by natural selection, and in time, some of its descendants might become water-dwellers altogether. In a similar way, the ancestors of the whale and the otter must slowly have become adapted to living in water.

At last, after disposing of numerous other objections, Darwin comes upon the most powerful objection of all: the fossil remains found in the geological record. He had not forgotten it. Indeed, he admits, it is "the most obvious and serious objection which can be urged against the theory." As we know, the transitional forms between modern species and extinct ancient species cannot be found in fossil remains, which show species appearing suddenly without any identifiable ancestors. If this is the true picture of the history of species, then the theory of evolution is false. If the theory of evolution is true, the fossil record must be imperfect.

In a celebrated chapter entitled "On the Imperfection of the Geological Record," Darwin proceeds to prove that the record is indeed incomplete. By means of a long and in-

The polecat Darwin cited as a case of a species in transition is actually the mink, now bred in quantities for its fur. In its wild state (above) the mink spends summer months in the water, catching fish, but in the winter it reverts to land life and a polecat's habit of preying on mice.

On the lichen-covered tree trunk that is its original habitat the peppered moth at top is well camouflaged, but in areas where industrial soot has blackened the oaks, the melanic variety below, which would be a freak under natural conditions, has been perpetuated by its dark pigmentation, making it invisible to an enemy.

volved geological argument, he shows that the fossil remains so far identified form only a small, misleading sample of the hundreds of thousands of species that once inhabited the globe. Nobody had previously realized that only an amazing combination of lucky circumstances enables any dying creature to leave a permanent record of its existence. The overwhelming number of living things have died without a trace. Even the vast majority of fossil traces are churned up and lost in the rising and falling of the earth's crust. Just because no transitional forms have been found, there is no reason to suppose that they never existed. The geological record is too imperfect for such a conclusion to be drawn from it. The most powerful weapon that can be used against the theory of evolution Darwin has now struck from his enemies' hands.

Now this extraordinary man enters the third and final stage of his long argument. To show his theory's power, he will use it to explain an immense variety of facts that have never been explained before. By the time he is done, virtually every fact known to naturalists will be seen in an utterly new light—the light of evolution, or "Darwinism," as it would soon be called.

Darwin begins this truly stupendous enterprise by looking once again at the geological record, which he has just exposed as a misleading picture of the history of living things. It does, however, reveal certain general truths, such as the fact that species become extinct. Although this fact is known to everyone, the death of species has never been satisfactorily explained. The answer used to be supernatural catastrophes, but now that geologists have rejected this, there simply is no explanation. The death of species is a "mystery," says Darwin, but a mystery that evolution can explain quite simply. In the struggle for existence, the emergence of a new species invariably results in the extinction of inferior rivals. The extinction of species, therefore, is exactly what we should *expect* to find in a world where species evolved by means of natural selection.

Another fact that creationists cannot explain is that the more ancient a species is, the less it resembles a modern species. If God created each species separately, there is no reason why they should resemble each other at all. An all-powerful Creator can design any kind of species He chooses. However, if modern species have evolved from ancient species, this fact is readily explained. As Darwin has already shown, species tend to grow less and less like their original parent species as more and more time goes by. Similarly, evolution explains why modern species in a particular area resemble the *recently* extinct species in the same area.

Now, Darwin turns to yet another broad category of facts that had never been adequately explained. For a long time scientists had been asking themselves why various species live in one part of the world and not in some other part. What, in other words, is the explanation for the present geographical distribution of plants and animals? The orthodox answer, says Darwin, is that the climate and the physical environment determine where species will live. He demolishes this explanation in one paragraph. As he points out, the physical environment of Australia, South Africa, and western South America are very much alike. One would expect, therefore, that similar plants and animals would be found in these places, whereas, in fact, "it would not be possible to point out three faunas and floras more utterly dissimilar." On the other hand, the rain forests of central South America are quite unlike the arid prairies of southerly South America. Therefore the species living in these two areas ought to be very different. In fact, they are quite similar. Obviously physical environment does not determine the geographical distribution of species. Yet this fact too and many more can be explained by evolution.

In general, Darwin's explanation is this: a new species or variety emerges by natural selection somewhere in the world. Being a superior form, it will increase its population locally at the expense of its competitors, then expand into new areas wherever it can beat out the local competition. When members of a species move into a new area, they are changing their living environment. Since these migrants will be waging a different battle for survival than members

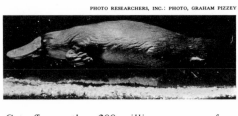

Cut off more than 200 million years ago from the rest of the world, the Australian continent contains many ancient and distinctive species. The duck-billed platypus (center) is a monotreme, an extremely primitive mammal that lays eggs but nurses its young on milk. The koala bear (left) and the kangaroo (above) are both marsupial mammals, whose young are nursed and carried in pouches until old enough to care for themselves. The koala, which limits its food strictly to young eucalyptus leaves, has become so specialized that it is more vulnerable to a changing environment than the hardy, herbivorous kangaroo, which flourishes wherever there is grass to be found.

of the same species who stayed at home, different variations will be useful to each in its particular struggle for life. Through the workings of natural selection the members of the parent species at home and those in the new locales will become, in time, so different that they will constitute distinct species. Because they are related, however, they will still look somewhat alike.

This is why species in the South American rain forests resemble those in the South American prairies: they are offspring of a common ancestor whose descendants spread into new places and so evolved in different ways. This is also why species in South America look so unlike the species in South Africa. Species could not spread across the great body of water that divides the two. The living things in South Africa and the living things in South America have descended, therefore, from different ancestors.

Darwin's theory also explains why remote oceanic islands like the Galápagos possess so many species found nowhere else and why these unique species nonetheless resemble the species on the nearest continent. This much Darwin had recognized a quarter of a century earlier, but now he applies his theory of natural selection to analyze certain other facts about the Galápagos that had originally baffled him. Their finches, Darwin had observed, are unique to the Galápagos archipelago. More baffling, however, is the fact that some of the finch species occur only on one or another of the islands in the chain, although physically the islands are exactly alike.

Darwin's explanation is that the islands of the archipelago were originally stocked by occasional migration of living things from the nearby continent. Obviously, such migrations are more or less lucky events, and it is therefore unlikely that any two islands will be stocked by exactly the same kind of migrants. As Darwin has already shown, the all-important factor for the survival of any living thing is its adjustment to its environment, to the other living things that surround it. Suppose that members of a certain bird species—some South American finches, for example—land on the island chain, some on one island, some on another. They will find themselves in somewhat different "webs of life," facing somewhat different competition from other migrants who have already become naturalized. The finches on one island may be forced to live on seeds because some other bird species already there is feeding on berries. On another island, the situation may be quite different. There, the finches may have to eat berries because seed-

*A German natural history picture book published in 1808 shows seven members of
the genus* Felis *from different parts of the world. Left to right from top, they are:
the American cougar, the African leopard, the Mexican ocelot, the European wild-
cat, the South American jaguar, the Tibetan tiger cat, and the Russian lynx.*

eating birds are already there. By natural selection, the seed-eating finches will evolve a large beak for devouring berries. Thus the mystery of those curious finch beaks is finally explained.

Having woven the geographical distribution of species into the gigantic web of the theory of evolution, Darwin tackles a category of facts that few biologists had previously thought of as even being facts. He explains the fundamental truth that all known species can be classified into groups on the basis of their physical resemblance.

This work of classifying living things was one of the proudest achievements of naturalists, and their classification system was quite elaborate. The ordinary household cat belongs, as we have seen, to the genus *Felis*, along with tigers, lions, and other cat species. The genus *Felis* belongs with other genera to a larger category yet, the "order" of Carnivora, or flesh-eaters. All the species in this order belong to an even larger category, the "class" known as

Mammalia, which includes all warm-blooded animals that suckle their young. Further, all the species in the great mammalian class belong to an even more basic group, the phylum of Chordates, which takes in all vertebrates, or animals with backbones. Although there are hundreds of thousands of animal species, there are only some twenty currently recognized phyla. (A similar classification holds for the plant kingdom.) Why should all this be so, asks Darwin. Why is it possible to classify every living thing into this elaborate pyramid of groups? Why does every animal species fall into just one of a handful of fundamental categories? Previous naturalists had never attempted to explain why. They were content to keep on classifying without wondering why it was possible. Yet, says Darwin, there is an explanation, and the explanation can only be evolution.

The only reason why any group of living things closely resemble each other is that they share a common ancestry. Species belonging to the same genus are similar because

Four of "Darwin's finches," the Galápagos birds that led the scientist to question accepted ideas about species, are pictured in an illustration from the official zoology of the Beagle *voyage. Far left, a variety that feeds on small insects has a neat, sharp bill. The variety next to it, which eats rather larger insects, has a broader but still pointed beak. The finch above, left, has evolved a heavier beak to peck at small seeds, but it is less blunt than that of the finch at right, which eats only large seeds.*

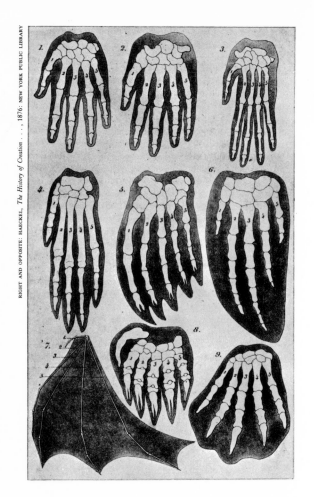

One of Darwin's strongest arguments for evolution was a comparison of features that are similar in all vertebrate mammals. These forefeet, or hands, in rows, from left to right, are those of man, gorilla, orangutan; dog, seal, porpoise; bat, mole, and duck-billed platypus, as illustrated in an 1876 treatise by Ernst Haeckel. This German scientist, an ardent advocate of Darwin's ideas, was chiefly responsible for his country's speedy acceptance of the Origin's *theories.*

they have a common ancient parent. It is the same with each category in the classification system. All the species belonging in the same order, class, or phylum have descended from a common ancestor. All the members of the phylum of Chordates, for example, have descended from some vertebrate animal that lived an immensely long time ago. Some of these primitive spined creatures evolved into reptiles, others into mammals. These were the ancestors of the Reptile and Mammal classes. Different mammal species evolved in various directions to form the orders and genera of the mammalian class. Thus, the naturalist's classification system is in fact a rough chart of the evolution of species.

And so Darwin proceeds to still more facts that had long puzzled students of nature. Why, for example, do the bones of the human hand bear such a close resemblance to the paddle of a porpoise, the wing of a bat, and the leg of a horse? These different species are extremely unlike, yet these parts of their respective bodies are composed of the same number of bones set in a similar position. Once again, the theory of evolution solves the mystery. Human beings, porpoises, bats, and horses are all mammals and have inherited this basic bone structure from a common parent.

Why are the human embryo, the embryo of a dog, and the embryo of a fish so startlingly alike? The only convincing explanation is descent from the same ancestor.

Why do so many living things have physical features that are totally useless to them, as, for example, the body hair on human males, or the teeth that lie under the gums of baby whales? Again, the answer is evolution. Physical features that were once useful have now become useless. Without evolution to explain this, men would have to say God created useless organs merely for the sake of doing so.

In this relentless fashion Darwin continues, page after page, churning out simple explanations of seemingly inexplicable facts. At last, however, even *The Origin of Species* must draw to a close. It has been a truly titanic effort. Roaming across the entire field of biology, Darwin has applied his theory to one great class of facts after another: from the geological record to comparative anatomy, from embryology to the geographical distribution of living things, from the study of useless organs to the system of classification. Everywhere, the theory of evolution provides concise and powerful explanations. Where once there had been a chaos of facts, vaguely attributed to the will of the Creator, now there is order and unity. As Darwin rightly remarks at the end of his long and difficult masterpiece: "It can hardly be supposed that a false theory" could explain so much so well.

This, in essence, is the basis of Darwin's whole argument: a false theory could not explain so much. Nor could a false theory overcome so many sharp and critical objections that Darwin himself has hurled at it. As for the theory itself, it has been built upon a solid foundation of two remarkably simple facts: the high birth rate of living things and the existence of small, hereditary variations. From these two basic facts Darwin has constructed a whole new evolutionary world. It is a world where natural selection has become a substitute for the Creator, and where life is being constantly destroyed. Even man himself—as Darwin hints—is but a superior animal evolved in the struggle for existence. In 1859 this was a truly terrifying picture, and so the question remained to be answered: Would the long, relentless argument of *The Origin of Species* really persuade men to accept what they so desperately wished to reject?

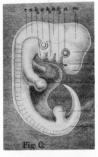

Further proof of man's evolution from more primitive species comes from the close resemblance between the embryos, from top to bottom, of tortoise, chick, dog, and man at early stages in their development.

VII

CONTROVERSY
AND CONQUEST

In November, 1859, when *The Origin of Species* appeared, there were only two "Darwinians" in the world; and one of them, Alfred Russel Wallace, was far away in the Dutch East Indies. Charles Darwin stood virtually alone to face the attacks of eminent scientists and respectable clergymen, attacks that were to find a ready forum in most of the reputable magazines. Ingrown prejudice and deep religious conviction, sheer misunderstanding and downright professional jealousy all tipped the scales against Darwin. On his side, all Darwin possessed was a book that was hard to understand and a theory that apparently dispensed with a Creator. "I fear I shall be greatly abused," he said mildly.

Darwin was certainly not built for fierce public combat. He was too shy even to argue with his friends, let alone stand up against eloquent and quick-witted antagonists. The very thought of it made him feel more ill than ever. He himself was a man who did his thinking slowly and often found it hard to express his ideas. "It is something unintelligible to me," he remarked at this time, "how any one can argue in public as orators do." As Darwin himself admitted, the first sentence that came to his mind was usually the worst possible way to say something. In October and November he sent out advance copies of his book to friends and scientific colleagues, in England and abroad. Then he retired to take a water cure in Yorkshire and wait for the battle to commence. He was a general scanning the horizon in search of a supporting army.

There were three men, above all, whom he wished to convert to his theory. If these three came round, Darwin said, "I should feel that the subject is safe, and all the world might rail, but that ultimately the theory of Natural Selection (though, no doubt, imperfect in its present condition, and embracing many errors) would prevail." These

Vanity Fair Album, July, 1869: NEW YORK PUBLIC LIBRARY

Vanity Fair, January, 1871: NEW YORK PUBLIC LIBRARY

A contemporary cartoonist depicted the chief antagonists in the debate over evolution: Bishop Wilberforce (left) and Thomas Huxley, whose belligerent pose expresses his opposition to the man known as "Soapy Sam."

three were Darwin's friends Joseph Hooker, the leading botanist in England; Sir Charles Lyell, the leading geologist; and thirty-four-year-old Thomas Henry Huxley, who was already the nation's foremost zoologist. Hooker and Lyell had read and criticized the book in each of its stages during the past year, but neither had been prepared to go all the way with him. Of Huxley, Darwin felt a little more hopeful. He sent each a copy of the *Origin* and then awaited their reactions as anxiously as a politician counting the votes on election night.

Hooker, after years of discussion with Darwin, was already a convert to evolution, though not to evolution by natural selection. That same November he had even published a botanical treatise that used evolution as a working hypothesis, the first scientific work to do so. About natural selection, however, Hooker had reservations. It could not, he insisted, be the only cause of evolutionary change.

Lyell was another, and sadder, case. There was no one, Darwin believed, who carried more weight with scientists than his old friend and advisor. "Remember that your verdict," Darwin told the sixty-two-year-old geologist, "will probably have more influence than my book in deciding whether such views as I hold will be admitted or rejected at present." Alas, what made Lyell so influential was the very thing that made it so hard for him to reach a verdict. As he sadly explained to friends, he was the nation's "champion of anti-transmutation." Most men looked to Lyell to refute Darwin's theory, not to defend it.

The old geologist was in a most unhappy predicament. It was hard enough for him to renounce his old beliefs, but to renounce the very beliefs that made him famous was painful indeed. Poor, compromising Lyell could never quite make up his mind. After reading a strong letter from Darwin, he would feel ready to renounce creationism. Then he would mull over his old arguments and lapse, he said sheepishly, into his old creationist views. He could accept evolution only if God, and not natural selection, were the cause of evolutionary change. In spite of Lyell's rather confused beliefs, Darwin counted the aging geologist as one of his allies. "Lyell is nearly a convert," he reported happily in November, but "nearly" was all Lyell would ever be.

Matters went quite differently with Huxley, who had no fear of dangerous ideas and who never hesitated about anything. Nimble-minded and self-confident, Huxley, a friend said, "was always mobilized for action." What is more, the action he enjoyed most was a fight, especially a

Lyell found it hard to accept Darwin's evolutionary theories because, to him, belief in natural selection meant he must renounce belief in God as man's Creator. The idea of viewing the orangutan (above) as a near relation of the human species was so distasteful that he could not, as he informed Darwin, "go the whole orang."

fight against respectable ideas. Even before the appearance of Darwin's book, Huxley had not been an orthodox creationist. He had not been an evolutionist either, because no one could tell him how evolution occurred. Curiously enough, some years before, he had brashly criticized evolution to Darwin's face. "I was not aware, at that time," Huxley recalled, "that he had then been many years brooding over the species-question; and the humorous smile which accompanied his gentle answer that such was not altogether his view, long haunted and puzzled me."

Now, when Huxley read Darwin's explanation of evolution, he knew the reason for that humorous smile. Huxley saw instantly, as Darwin had before him, that natural selection was not only the key to evolution, it was also a splendidly simple one. "How extremely stupid," he exclaimed, "not to have thought of that!" As soon as he had finished reading *The Origin of Species*, Huxley dashed off a letter to its author. "I am prepared to go to the stake for evolution," he announced in his confident way. "As to the curs which will bark and yelp, you must recollect that some of your friends, at any rate, are endowed with an amount of combativeness which (though you have often and justly rebuked it) may stand you in good stead. I am sharpening up my claws and beak in readiness."

The entire first edition of the *Origin*—1250 copies—was sold out the first day, and the publisher, Murray, asked Darwin to prepare a new edition. Elated by the support of the friends he most valued, Darwin claimed he felt "as bold as a lion." Meanwhile, the anti-Darwinian forces were gathering their strength. As a sign of what was to come, Darwin, in December, received a savage letter from his old Cambridge friend and teacher Adam Sedgwick, professor of geology and canon of Norwich cathedral. "I have read your book with more pain than pleasure," wrote Sedgwick. "Parts of it I admired greatly, parts I laughed at till my sides were almost sore; other parts I read with absolute sorrow, because I think them utterly false and grievously mischievous." The theory, cried Sedgwick, "would sink the human race into a lower grade of degradation than any into which it has fallen since its written record tells us of its history." In Sedgwick's opinion, Darwin was not even an honest scientist: he was simply a vicious atheist in disguise. Similar attacks were made by the Archbishop of Dublin and by lesser clergymen: evolution was "degrading," evolution was "materialistic," evolution proclaimed that "there is no God and the ape is our Adam."

Sightseeing Victorian families climb the stairs of the British Museum to study the impressive display of stuffed animals in the natural history section, Owen's domain.

Attacks from pious clergymen Darwin had more or less expected, although he had one very friendly letter from the Reverend Charles Kingsley, the novelist, to whom he had sent a copy of his book. In the letter Kingsley spoke for those who were able to reconcile evolution with belief in God when he admitted that he had "learnt to see that it is just as noble a conception of Deity to believe that He created primal forms capable of self-development into all forms needful . . . as to believe that He required a fresh act of intervention to supply the lacunas [gaps] which He Himself had made. I question whether the former be not the loftier thought."

The scientific reactions, however, which poured into Down House in the weeks that followed the book's publication, disturbed Darwin greatly. He scarcely knew what to make of them. One scientist told him that he would read the *Origin*, "but I will never believe it"—a strange admission of prejudgment for a scientist to make. Nor could Darwin understand another scientist who told him his theory must be false because it explained so much—the very reason Darwin believed it was true. When, in December, Darwin made one of his rare trips to London, he was no longer feeling so bold.

Calling at the British Museum, where many of his old scientific colleagues worked, Darwin felt as if he were entering enemy territory. A young biologist, working in the museum's insect room, overheard him say cheerily to a friend: "Good morning, Mr. White—I'm afraid you won't speak to me any more." To which Adam White replied sadly, "Ah, Sir! if ye had only stopped with the *Voyage of the Beagle*." Adam White, at least, merely grieved over an old friend's mistakes. Later that day a clergyman spied Darwin's tall, stooped figure in another room and described him as "the most dangerous man in England."

The British Museum was in truth enemy territory, for the museum's paleontology department was headed by Sir Richard Owen, a man who was determined to discredit Darwin's theory with every weapon at his command. Himself a disciple of Cuvier, and the world's leading authority on extinct forms of life, Owen knew full well how powerfully Darwin had stated his ideas about evolution. He was also an old acquaintance of Darwin's since the days when they had worked together to identify the fossil specimens from the *Beagle* voyage, and he understood just how long and how honestly Darwin had labored to construct his theory. When Darwin came round to call on him at the museum, Owen greeted him warmly, for he was a sly and devious man, wise in the ways of the world.

Owen was a man of humble birth, whose intense ambition and genuine ability had made him, at fifty-five, a protégé of the royal family, an advisor to prime ministers, a friend of the rich, the famous, and the noble. Dukes invited Owen to spend weekends at their country estates, and foreign princes visited him to exchange views with one of England's brightest scientific luminaries. Yet despite his extraordinary success, Owen was extremely jealous of the scientific achievements of others. Lesser men than Darwin aroused his envy, and he was not above stealing other men's discoveries and publishing them as his own.

Professional jealousy, however, was only one of Owen's motives. Another was his fear of losing all that he had worked so hard to win. He was the darling of polite society, and polite society detested the theory of evolution. Indeed, an article in one leading magazine virtually ordered Owen to attack Darwin's theory. For the moment, however, Owen bided his time.

Owen was not the only scientist with unscientific motives for rejecting Darwin's theory. For years, naturalists had followed Paley in proclaiming that science was the loyal ally of religious faith. The analysis of the structure of living things, it was said, demonstrated the wisdom of the Creator, while the study of how each species is adapted to its environment demonstrated His goodness. Unfortunately, as we have seen, Darwin's theory destroyed the foundation of this argument. The alliance between science and religion was endangered, as one writer openly complained. Darwinism, he said, had been "thrust upon us at this time of day, when science has walked in calm majesty out from the mists of prejudice, and been accepted as a sister by a sound theology." By attacking Darwin's theory, many scientists were defending their position as respectable supporters of religious faith.

One such scientist, who now made his views felt, was Louis Agassiz of Harvard University, a Swiss-born geologist who had been for many years a shining ornament of Boston intellectual society. That science was theology's "sister" was Agassiz' lifelong conviction. The facts about living things, he used to tell his students, "proclaim aloud the one God, whom man may know, adore, and love; and Natural History must, in good time, become the analysis of the thoughts of the Creator of the Universe, as manifested in the animal and vegetable kingdoms." This kind of pious

Mistrustful, like Darwin, of Sir Richard Owen's integrity, the American philosopher Ralph Waldo Emerson once wrote of the paleontologist's "surgical smile." In an 1872 cartoon, Owen is mounted on a favorite hobbyhorse, the fossilized bones of a Megatherium.

science was very reassuring and Louis Agassiz was looked upon as "the prince of naturalists."

Darwin, who was well aware of Agassiz' views, had sent him a copy of the *Origin* with a courteous note asking the Harvard geologist at least to give him credit for "having earnestly endeavoured to arrive at the truth." He expected Agassiz to disagree violently, and he was not disappointed. In January, 1860, Agassiz announced to members of the Boston Natural History Society that Darwin's new doctrine was "an ingenious but fanciful theory." "The arguments presented by Darwin's book," he assured his admirers, " . . . have not made the least impression on my mind."

Nor could they make the least impression, for Agassiz' mind was shut tight. To him evolution was not a theory, it was a threat: a danger to religion, a danger to science, and above all, a danger to Louis Agassiz, who had staked his whole reputation on the belief that each species is "a thought of God." He held a series of debates at the Natural History Society, with Asa Gray, professor of botany at Harvard, staunchly supporting Darwin and his theory. A few of Agassiz' admirers were appalled to see the great man twist and turn, trip over facts, and contradict his own statements in his determination to discredit evolution. "He must strangle it at birth," remarked one observer, after seeing how blindly Agassiz rejected what was, after all, the serious life's work of an honest fellow scientist. But Agassiz was not unique: scientists in France and Germany refused to discuss evolution at all.

By the spring of 1860, Darwin's confidence that his theory would prevail was becoming badly shaken. Attacks on his theory were growing more bold, while his own few supporters had not yet spoken out in public.

Even Huxley, whom Darwin had called "my good and admirable agent for the promulgation of damnable heresies," had not openly declared himself a Darwinian. All he had said so far, in an anonymous review of the *Origin* in the London *Times*, was that Darwin's "hypothesis" should be treated with respect. Hooker was saying the same thing to fellow botanists, but he did not say it in public. In America, it was true, Asa Gray was "fighting like a Trojan," said Darwin, against Agassiz' minions, but Gray, too, found Darwinism too materialistic. As for Lyell, he openly complained that "Darwin's hypothesis (I claim no higher place for it)" was merely a variation on Lamarck's, which annoyed Darwin extremely. As far as the public was concerned, the anti-Darwinians held the field.

Another eminent opponent of Darwin's idea was Louis Agassiz, a brilliant Swiss naturalist, who was the first foreign-born professor to teach at Harvard. Agassiz (above) possessed the unusual gift of being able to draw faultless diagrams while he lectured.

In one scientific conference after another, the theory was discussed, ridiculed, and rejected. One man termed the theory useless because it did not explain how the *first* living thing came to be. Many scientists understood Darwinism so little that they dismissed it as inferior to the "transformism" of Lamarck. At least Lamarck, said one, gave a cause for evolution, while "Mr. Darwin does no such thing." To this critic, natural selection was not even a cause, while other scientists called it a mysterious power that Darwin had invented out of whole cloth. "I must be an extremely bad explainer," Darwin concluded glumly.

The numerous distortions of Darwin's theory were leaving the impression that Darwinism was a weak and futile idea unworthy of serious attention. In March, for example, readers of the influential weekly *The Spectator* were offered a reassuring essay entitled "Objections to Mr. Darwin's Theory." They learned that Darwin's long and intricate argument for evolution was nothing but "a string of air bubbles," and that Darwin's massive accumulation of evidence carried no weight at all. As the author pointed out, Darwin's indirect method of proof—starting with the theory and then showing how much it can explain—was ingenious and clever but it was not the "true" method of science. The anonymous author of this essay was Adam Sedgwick, who had written it originally as a private letter to the Archbishop of Dublin. A fanatic on the topic of Darwinism, the Archbishop sent it to *The Spectator* for publication. Sedgwick did not even mind seeing his confidence betrayed. In fact, he told his friends, he was pleased.

A few weeks after Sedgwick's article appeared, a far more devastating blow was struck against Darwin and his theory. This time, Richard Owen himself took the field. His weapon was a forty-five-page review in the April issue of the illustrious *Edinburgh Review*. Under a cloak of anonymity, Owen penned an attack so slyly dishonest and so actively malicious that it still has the power to infuriate.

Purring with false friendliness, the anonymous writer declares that he has found three "important and original observations" in *The Origin of Species*. They are "gems," he says, worthy of the author's talents. And what are these gems so deserving of praise? Three observations made by Darwin about ants and bees! There is nothing else praiseworthy in *The Origin of Species*. "Having now cited the chief, if not the whole, of the original observations adduced by its author in the volume now before us, our disappointment may be conceived." The theory, says Owen in mock

Punch, MAY, 1861: NEW YORK PUBLIC LIBRARY

MONKEYAN'A.

AM I A MAN AND A BROTHER?

Am I satyr or man?
Pray tell me who can,
And settle my place in the scale.
A man in ape's shape,
An anthropoid ape,
Or monkey deprived of his tail?

The *Vestiges* taught,
That all came from naught
By "development," so called, "progressive;"
That insects and worms
Assume higher forms
By modification excessive.

Then DARWIN set forth.
In a book of much worth,
The importance of "Nature's selection;"
How the struggle for life
Is a laudable strife,
And results in "specific distinction."

Let pigeons and doves
Select their own loves,
And grant them a million of ages,
Then doubtless you'll find
They've altered their kind,
And changed into prophets and sages.

One of the earliest cartoon reactions to the evolution controversy was this poem, published in the humorous weekly Punch *in 1861. It refers both to* Vestiges *and to Darwin's "book of much worth."*

sorrow, is simply no good. The reader, however, must take Owen's word for this, because he carefully omits to describe it. In this way he is free to cover forty-five pages with misrepresentations of Darwin's theory.

One of Owen's tactics is to attribute some idea to Darwin that Darwin never had. Then he shows, with a sneer, that the idea is false. How can we credit natural selection, he asks, when variant offspring are freaks and freaks are too feeble to survive in competition? This is a sound criticism, although Darwin insisted that random variations are extremely tiny ones. Large and freakish is exactly what they are not.

Elsewhere Owen remarks that Darwin asks for belief in his theory *because* the geological record is imperfect, and in fact, that he rests his theory on the lack of evidence in favor of it! What Darwin actually said, of course, was that the evidence from fossil remains was too incomplete to be used *against* his theory. Owen, however, does not let the truth stand in his way. By clever innuendoes he contrives to leave the impression that Darwin is some kind of fumbling amateur who is beneath the contempt of serious scientists. He remarks, for example, that "the complex web of life" is an interesting idea, which can be found in poems, thereby implying that that is where Darwin found it.

In conclusion, Owen decides that the theory is purely conjectural. Then what, one might ask, does he make of the evidence Darwin has amassed in support of his "conjecture"? To this question Owen has a perfect answer: he omits to mention such evidence. Natural selection, he sums up, "is just one of those obvious possibilities that might float through the imagination of any speculative naturalist; only, the sober searcher after truth would prefer a blameless silence to sending the proposition forth as explanatory of the origin of species (without its inductive foundation)." As if such brazen lies were not sufficient, Owen devotes long passages of his essay to praising a certain great "working naturalist" by the name of Professor Richard Owen!

The unscrupulous attack in the *Edinburgh Review* left Darwin shaken and angry, but not so shaken that he did not recognize the author. "It is extremely malignant [and] clever," he wrote Lyell, "and I fear will be very damaging . . . It is painful to be hated in the intense degree to which Owen hates me."

Owen, however, was far from done yet. The most important scientific event of the year was to take place at the

Scene of the epic confrontation at the British Association's 1860 meeting was Oxford's University Museum. This glass-roofed, high-arched structure was built around mid-century to house the university's scientific collections, and as can be seen from this modern photograph, a truly Victorian mixture of specimens fills its halls.

end of June: the annual meeting of the British Association for the Advancement of Science. These British Association meetings were no ordinary scholarly conferences. The week-long gatherings were gala affairs, attended not only by scientists but by large numbers of admiring private citizens as well. They had become an annual advertisement for science in which scientists could show just how beneficial their work was to the nation's well-being.

Clearly, such a meeting was a fine occasion for science to demonstrate its respectability and crush Darwinism once and for all. Nor would Owen even have to strike the blow himself. This year the meetings were to be held at Oxford University, and the Bishop of Oxford himself was eager to make a public stand against Darwinism.

Glib-tongued and witty, Bishop Samuel Wilberforce—"Soapy Sam" to his critics—had great faith in his ability, claiming that all he needed was some coaching in biology. Professor Owen, of course, was delighted to oblige him. The pair had already collaborated on a damning anonymous review of Darwin's book to be published in the *Quarterly Review* for July, and the British Association meeting would provide an ideal introduction. Owen studiously crammed the Bishop with arguments to hurl against Darwin, and thanks to his efforts, a climactic clash over evolution was about to take place, on a field decidedly unfavorable to Darwin.

The result was to be one of the most memorable scenes in the history of science, a drama starring Thomas Huxley and a large cast of supporting characters, each of whom played his part to perfection. The only actor missing was Darwin himself. Ill and depressed, he had gone to Sudbury Park, Richmond, to take yet another water cure two days before the meetings began. The setting of the drama bore the prosaic name of "Section D," the Botany and Zoology section of the British Association. By a quirk of good fortune for Darwin's supporters, the presiding officer of the section was Darwin's old teacher Professor Henslow.

Although the Bishop was not due to speak until the third day of the meeting, there was a brief opening skirmish at the first session on Thursday, June 28. Henslow, out of kindness for his former student Darwin, asked Huxley for some remarks about Darwinism. Looking round at an audience so openly hostile to evolution, Huxley declined to speak. Prejudice, he said, would interfere with any serious scientific discussion. Owen replied that he for one would make no appeal to prejudice and would speak "in the spirit of the philosopher." Whereupon he proceeded to attack Darwinism at exactly the point on which prejudice was strongest: the question of the origin of man. The structure of the human brain, said Owen, proved that man could not be classified as a kinsman of the apes—which was just what the audience wished to hear. Huxley swiftly rose and contradicted Owen flatly to his face. He would, he promised, demolish Owen's facts at some future date. This was as close to being a declaration of war as men usually make at scientific assemblies.

The next day, Friday, nothing controversial occurred, and Huxley decided he would leave Oxford on Saturday. He was not going to sit around, he said, to be "episcopally pounded" by the Bishop of Oxford. It was almost impossible, he knew, to strike back at a bishop in a public debate. That evening Huxley was striding restlessly through Oxford's narrow streets, when, quite by chance, he came upon none other than Robert Chambers, the secret author of the much-battered *Vestiges of the Natural History of Creation.* When the old evolutionist heard that Huxley intended to leave town, he pleaded with him passionately "not to desert us," for Huxley was the only Darwinian with any real talent for a fight. The passionate plea startled Huxley out of his decision. "I'll come," he told Chambers, "and have my share of what is going on."

The next morning, Saturday, excitement was at fever pitch. More than seven hundred people thronged the lecture room. The crowd was so huge that the meeting was rescheduled for the library of the University Museum. There, dominating the center of the room, sat a small army of clergymen, ready to cheer their Bishop on. Lining the window ledges was a bevy of excitable ladies, equally eager

AN ASSOCIATION FOR THE ADVANCEMENT OF SCIENCE ON AN EXCURSION.

John Leech's caricature of a British Association field trip presents a very unscientific view of that august body's diversions. At center, a geologist uses his hammer to open one of several bottles of wine being enjoyed by the company, while in the distance eminent scientists and their ladies disport themselves on the beach.

131

John Stevens Henslow was sixty-four years old when he presided over the Wilberforce-Huxley debate. Although he himself could not believe in evolution, his natural fair-mindedness demanded that Darwin's viewpoint be heard.

to see evolution demolished. In a far corner sat a mischievous knot of undergraduates who had come to shout about anything worth shouting about. The Darwinians in the gathering were an extremely tiny minority, but two of them, Huxley and Hooker, sat on the platform alongside the Bishop of Oxford.

Before the Bishop spoke, however, the audience had to suffer impatiently through a long-winded speech, "The Intellectual Development of Europe considered with reference to the views of Mr. Darwin," by John William Draper, an American historian. After that, an unfortunate scientist named Dingle went to the blackboard to describe evolution mathematically: "Let this point A be man," said Dingle, in a pronounced regional accent, "and let this point B be the mawnkey." This was as far as he got. "Mawnkey! Mawnkey!" jeered the undergraduates, and poor Dingle had to sit down. At long last, it was Bishop Wilberforce's turn to speak. Tall and lean and garbed in stately black, the Bishop of Oxford advanced to the podium.

"The permanence of specific forms," he announced, coolly reciting all Owen's arguments, "is a fact confirmed by all observations." Had anyone ever seen, he smoothly inquired, a single case of a species evolving? Species today were what species had always been, he assured the vast audience, and Darwin's theory was "the merest hypothesis supported by the most unbridled assumptions." With perfect ease, the Bishop moved lightly from one point to another, ridiculing Darwin and heaping scorn upon Huxley, whom he wished to wound for his earlier contradiction of Owen. Can we really believe, the Bishop inquired sweetly, "that all favorable varieties of turnip are tending to become men?" Such was the general scoffing tone of the Bishop's speech, a tone so light, so sure, and so witty that the audience was swept powerfully along. The evolutionists, he remarked toward the close of his speech, must be men with a preference for having apes as their ancestors.

Then, turning toward Huxley, the Bishop asked, with an insolent smile, whether it was through his grandfather or his grandmother that Huxley himself claimed his descent from a monkey? With this rude remark, the Bishop had blundered and Huxley saw it in a flash. "The Lord hath delivered him into mine hands," he whispered to a neighbor.

The audience, however, loved it and applauded the Bishop loudly. The ladies waved their handkerchiefs vigorously in response to their episcopal champion. As Bishop Wilberforce returned triumphantly to his seat, Huxley re-

A popular Parisian fashion magazine, widely circulated in England, suggested these modes for early summer of 1860—the period of the Darwinian dispute. The lady at right is in walking costume, while her seated friend, in an afternoon dress, has added an unwittingly up-to-the-minute touch of elegance: a monkey on a leash.

solved "to let him have it." With the instincts of a born actor, he slowly rose and began to answer the Bishop in a voice full of somber dignity. To each of the Bishop's empty arguments he delivered a polite but pointed rebuttal. Indeed, Huxley remarked, there was nothing new in the Bishop's speech except the question about "my personal predilections in the matter of ancestry." For that, said Huxley, he had an answer too. "If the question is put to me, 'Would I rather have a miserable ape for a grandfather, or a man highly endowed by nature and possessed of great means and influence, and yet who employs these faculties and that influence for the mere purpose of introducing ridicule into a grave scientific discussion'—I unhesitatingly affirm my preference for the ape."

Pandemonium broke loose in the audience; a certain Lady Brewster fainted and had to be carried out. For some minutes nobody could be heard, as the audience babbled wildly over Huxley's retort to the Bishop. Then a man strode to the platform and lifted a huge volume of the Bible over his head. "The Book! The Book," he shouted. "Divine Revelation is all! Human science is nothing!" He had pleaded with Darwin, he said, never to forsake the Bible. Here indeed was a voice from the past, for the fervent speaker was Robert Fitzroy. It was a curious epilogue to the voyage of the *Beagle*.

The commotion infused Joseph Hooker with a surge of fighting spirit such as he had never felt in his life. "I swore to myself," he later reported to Darwin, "that I would smite that Amalekite Sam, hip and thigh if my heart jumped out of my mouth." Luckily, kindly old Henslow called upon Hooker to speak, and the audience that had come to jeer at Darwin now heard the nation's finest botanist dismantle Bishop Wilberforce and expose his arguments once again as worthless. The Bishop sat stunned and speechless; he had blundered into a hornet's nest of Darwinians—"leaving you master of the field," Hooker wrote Darwin, "after 4 hours' battle."

When Darwin heard the news, he was delighted, although it was beyond him, he said, how Huxley and Hooker could be so bold. "I would as soon have died as tried to answer the Bishop in such an assembly." Most of all Darwin was deeply moved by the loyalty of his friends. "I was low enough," he now wrote to Hooker, "and thinking what a useless burthen I was to myself and all others, when your letter came, and it has so cheered me; your kindness and affection brought tears into my eyes . . . I have read so many hostile views," he went on, "that I was beginning to think that perhaps I was wholly in the wrong, and that Owen was right when he said the whole subject would be forgotten in ten years; but now that I hear that you and Huxley will fight publicly (which I am sure I never could do), I fully believe that our cause will, in the long run, prevail."

Darwin was right, more right than he knew. The fact that two of England's leading scientists had spoken out so sensationally in support of the theory left its mark on their colleagues. After Huxley and Hooker had spoken, honest men could no longer take *The Origin of Species* lightly or sneer at the theory without first trying to understand it. This was all, really, that Darwin had ever asked: that scientists might read with honest care the long, complex argument for evolution by natural selection that he had

A DARWINIAN IDEA.

SUGGESTED BY THE CATTLE SHOW.

THE OLD SORT.

THE MODERN IMPROVEMENT.

WHAT IT MUST COME TO.

An 1865 Punch *cartoon, presenting a pig evolving by stages into a living ham with only snout and tail remaining, shows how quickly Darwin's 1859 theory of evolution had gained a general circulation.*

spent half his lifetime in composing. In the battle over evolution the Oxford meeting was to mark the turning of the tide.

Men continued, it is true, to rail savagely against "the monkey theory," as evolution was often called. Polite society still preferred to side with the "angels" and not with the "apes," as one current joke put it. To numerous nonscientists the theory remained a threat to faith and to what they took to be the dignity of man. Even Erasmus Darwin's good friend Thomas Carlyle, the historian, referred to Darwinism as a "gospel of dirt."

It was true, too, that most of the older scientists continued to call the theory conjectural, and in the United States, Louis Agassiz never stopped lecturing against evolution. "The Darwinian Theory utterly demolished by AGASSIZ HIMSELF" ran the advertisement for these lectures. But it really did not matter any more. In the wake of the Oxford meeting, the signs of Darwin's triumph were emerging all around.

At Harvard, Agassiz' own students pored over *The Origin of Species* when the professor's back was turned, and in truth, this was the most important sign of all. Whatever older scientists might say, young scientists everywhere read Darwin with enthusiasm and awe. Their minds were fresh and they had no reputations to defend. To men starting scientific careers, the theory of evolution opened vast new fields for exploration. The old theory did not. To side with the "angels" might be dignified, but to side with the "apes" was more exciting.

Within a year or two of the *Origin*'s appearance, the old creationist doctrine was virtually a dead letter. Many scientists still looked skeptically upon natural selection, but few first-rate men now doubted that species had evolved. Eventually, said Darwin, such men would come to accept natural selection, too. At the British Association meetings in 1861 and 1862, Huxley destroyed Owen's old argument about the uniqueness of the human brain and exposed Owen himself as a cheat who had used discredited facts to build up his case against Darwinism. Darwin's most malicious foe was thus struck down. Ironically, people now flocked to Owen's own exhibits in the British Museum, asking to see the "varieties" that Mr. Darwin had said were species in the making. By 1863, the Reverend Charles Kingsley could write to a friend that "Darwin is conquering everywhere and rushing in like a flood, by the mere force of truth and fact."

The gentle recluse of Down had triumphed after all.

THE LION OF THE SEASON.
Alarmed Flunkey. "MR. G-G-G-O-O-O-RILLA!"

In 1861 Punch *satirized the uproar over man's close relationship to the apes by portraying a startled footman announcing the season's most honored guest: a whitegloved gorilla in full evening dress.*

VIII

DARWIN TRIUMPHANT

The twenty-two years that Darwin lived after the launching of his theory were, on the whole, fruitful and contented. They were quiet years as well, although he was fast becoming one of the most celebrated men in the world. The temptations of fame, however, made no change in the unswerving routine of Down House, nor did they make any change in Darwin's sane and simple character. This was because the inhabitants of Down House did not much care about fame. "I sometimes find it very odd," Emma Darwin remarked one day, "that anyone belonging to me should be making such a noise in the world."

Still, there was one important change in Darwin's life, for something like a holiday spirit now pervaded the Down House routine. The theory of evolution, which had dominated Darwin's thinking for a quarter of a century, was no longer his own private burden. The theory now belonged to the world, and it was making its way triumphantly. No longer need he fear that his great life's work might in the end prove a failure. The fear had lain like a dark shadow across his path, but the shadow at long last had been lifted. Darwin was freer now than he had been since the idea of evolution had first taken hold of his mind. He could do as he liked—and what he liked, as always, was science.

Compared to the mighty theory of evolution, however, it was often science on a small scale. In May, 1862, for example, Darwin published the results of research he had been conducting throughout the raging controversy over evolution. Surprisingly enough, the book was not about evolution at all, at least not directly. It was a learned treatise on orchids, and it bore the scholarly title *On The*

"The new hothouse is ready, and I long to stock it, just like a schoolboy," *Darwin told Hooker in 1863. A modern Russian artist has re-created one of* *the scientist's daily visits to check his intricate experiments on orchids.*

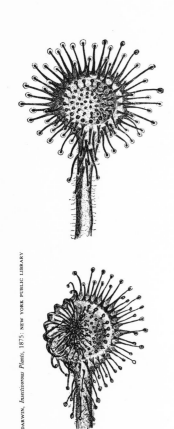

Observing that sundew plants caught insects on platelike leaves like the one at top, Darwin began studying how and why they did so. He discovered that when some of the sundew's sticky tentacles trapped a fly, they would bend (below) to cover the fly until their fluid not only killed it but also "ate" it by absorbing its nutrients into the plant's own tissues.

Various Contrivances by Which British and Foreign Orchids are Fertilized by Insects. In this work, Darwin showed for the first time that the beautiful orchid flower is actually a highly useful structure, which lures insects to the plants and sticks the gluey orchid pollen to the insects' bodies to be transported to other orchid plants. Darwin referred to his orchid study as his "hobbyhorse," for real work, in his eyes, was work on the theory of evolution. After the orchid study was done, however, the investigation of climbing plants became his next hobby, and after that he investigated insect-eating plants and made delicate experiments to discover how these curious plants could act, as he said, like "an animal in disguise."

This research gives the true measure of Darwin's deep humility and of the purity of his love for science. Another man, after revolutionizing science with a great theory, might have retired in glory or spent the rest of his life expounding and interpreting his theory before a vast, admiring public. That task Darwin gladly left to the crusading Thomas Huxley. He himself was perfectly content to stay at Down House, quietly pursuing his botanical work.

Whether the subject was great or small did not matter very much to Darwin. He loved making observations about living things and he loved devising theories to explain them. Indeed, his plant experiments delighted him so much that he decided to build a hothouse in order to raise all kinds of plants and to be able to work in all seasons of the year.

This new addition also supplied the Darwins' children with another jest for their collection of family jokes about "Papa." The expression on Darwin's face when he brooded over his plants was known to the children now as his "hothouse face," and they could tell how well the experiments were going just by looking at their father. The Down House gardener, on the other hand, was completely mystified by his employer's botanical researches. Once, when a caller asked him how Darwin was feeling, the gardener replied: "Oh, my poor master has been very sadly. I often wish he had something to do. He moons about the garden and I have seen him standing doing nothing before a flower for ten minutes at a time."

By now most of Darwin's children were reaching adulthood. In 1865 William, the eldest, passed his twenty-sixth birthday and was on his way to becoming a wealthy banker. Henrietta, who was twenty-two that year, was old enough to serve as her father's editor and secretary. The youngest son, Horace, was only fourteen at the time, but he had already astonished his father by understanding natural selection better than did a good many scientists. Eventually, Horace became an engineer, while George, who was then twenty, later became an astronomer. In truth, the little world of Down House was changing, in spite of Darwin's wish that it might remain forever the same. As one sign of change, the boys decided one day that they were too old to call him "Papa" any more and would address him as "Father" instead. "I would sooner be called Dog," Darwin glumly complained.

There was no holding back the years, of course, and Darwin was growing ever more stooped and gray. After publishing *The Origin of Species*, he had grown a long beard, which made him look like a sage, or as his sons said, like Moses. He was not sure that he really looked quite so old and so wise. Certainly he did not often act like a wise old man, for in spite of the passing years, his outlook remained invincibly boyish. He loved, for example, to pretend that his nightly games of backgammon with Emma were titanic struggles, and for years he kept a careful record of all the wins and losses. "The tally with my wife in backgammon stands thus," he once reported to Asa Gray in America, "She, poor creature, has won only 2,490 games, whilst I have won, hurrah, hurrah, 2,795 games."

Darwin, however, had one serious task to perform before his work in evolution was done. In 1867 he decided that the time had come to speak out on the most crucial topic embraced by the theory of evolution: the burning question of the origin of man. This subject had been fiercely debated in public ever since November, 1859, but Darwin had said almost nothing about it in *The Origin of Species*. That work was controversial enough, he believed, without dragging into it the explosive question of man's origin. Since that time Charles Lyell had demonstrated that man had inhabited the world one hundred thousand years ago, and Thomas Huxley had proved in a brilliant essay that man was a full-fledged member of the animal kingdom. The question, nonetheless, remained: Could the human species, with its amazing powers of mind, have been produced by evolution through natural selection?

Darwin himself had no doubt that this was the case and he now decided to touch upon the subject in a general way. What he had in mind was a brief chapter on man, to be included in a long treatise he was writing called *Variation of Animals and Plants Under Domestication*. This enormous compilation supplied naturalists with all the basic data

As Darwin's reputation increased, scientists began asking for interviews with the retiring invalid. Huxley, who often visited Down, added to a letter seeking an appointment for a friend this drawing of the hopeful visitor kneeling before "Pope" Darwin's throne.

THE MODERN THEORY OF THE DESCENT OF MAN.

In 1871 Darwin's disciple Ernst Haeckel elaborated the theory behind The Descent of Man *in this family tree. His enthusiasm led him into such wild speculations as including the platypus (18) and kangaroo (19) as ancestors of man. But in charting the emergence of the human species from a unicellular organism (1), through shell, eel, fish, reptile, and amphibian (15) stages to those of primitive mammal, monkey, and ape man, he was essentially correct.*

about artificial selection and hereditary variation that could not be fitted into *The Origin of Species*. It was part of the monumental treatise on evolution that Darwin had set aside in 1858 and that he had long promised to complete for the benefit of his fellow scientists. (In fact, he never managed to put the entire mass of research into publishable form.) The work appeared in 1868 but without the chapter on man. By that time the chapter had already grown into a "very small volume."

Then, in April, 1869, the subject of man suddenly took on a new and terrible urgency. That month Darwin was thunderstruck to read an article by Alfred Russel Wallace declaring that natural selection was incapable of explaining the origin of human intelligence. "No!!!" Darwin scrawled angrily in the margin of Wallace's article, and he underlined the word three times. "I hope," he wrote Wallace later, "you have not murdered too completely your own and my child." He himself had no intention whatever of deserting his "child," and the very small volume on man grew even larger. It was not until 1871 that the book finally appeared. It contained Darwin's magnificent demonstration of man's animal origin, and it was entitled *The Descent of Man*.

In this great work, the companion and supplement to *The Origin of Species*, Darwin drew once more on the vast body of material he had been gathering for decades. In a superb summary of the known facts, he shows, first, the close and intimate resemblance that exists between man's physical structure and that of other mammals, notably the apes. The mighty brain of man, for example, is approximately two and one-half times the size of a gorilla's, yet, says Darwin, "every chief fissure and fold in the brain of man has its analogy in that of the orang."

Another profound resemblance between man and other animals, Darwin notes, is revealed by the fact that man can catch diseases from apes and other lower animals and can infect them with his own diseases. This means that they must closely resemble each other in tissue and blood. Then, too, there is the fact that the human embryo bears a startling resemblance to the embryos of other mammals. What is more, the development of the human embryo in its mother's womb is paralleled step by step by that of the ape embryo and at some stages their development is identical. Such profound similarities surely cannot be coincidental.

Now Darwin deals with another category of striking resemblances between man and other mammals, the category

The range of Darwin's interests and publications was astonishing. These drawings—from an 1872 work analyzing the means by which man and animals express emotions—show disappointment, in the pouting chimpanzee (top), and pleasure at being caressed, in the fiercely grinning baboon below.

Darwin studied the behavior of his shepherd dog, Bob, as carefully as that of any experimental animal, noting that, when hostile, Bob walked stiffly upright with head raised and hair erect (top). Reassured, Bob's fur lies flat, his ears draw back, and with a "flexuous movement of his body" he happily paws at Darwin's leg.

known as rudimentary or partially developed organs. The last few vertebrae of man's spine, for example, bear a close similarity to the spinal structure of animals with tails, so close indeed, says Darwin, that they plainly represent what would be a tail in other vertebrate animals. The structure of the human ear—including the rudimentary muscles that enable some people to wiggle their ears—is curiously like that of chimpanzees and orangs. What is more, a tiny blunt point projects from the folded edge of the human ear, which, if the fold were turned upward, would stick up somewhat like the pointed ear of many mammals.

These and similar resemblances must also be explained, and as those familiar with *The Origin of Species* know, the only acceptable explanation of close resemblances between different species is that they have descended from a common ancestor. Since man, as Darwin shows, closely resembles the apes, it is plain that man and the apes—and the other members of the primate order to which man belongs—have evolved from the same ancient mammal ancestor: a creature possessing pointed ears and a tail, which its descendant man exhibits in the tiny point on the fold of his ear and in the last few vertebrae of his spine. Nor is there any reason to doubt that man has evolved by means of natural selection. As Darwin points out, human children, like other animal offspring, will vary from their parents. Human beings, like other animals, tend to multiply beyond their means of subsistence. Therefore, there must have been a struggle for existence among the ancestors of man, and hence the natural selection of favorable variations. Man, at least physically, is no exception to the rules that govern the evolution of all other species.

But what of man's enormously superior intellect? Is it true, as even Wallace believed, that human intelligence was a special gift bestowed upon the human animal by the Creator? No, says Darwin, and he proceeds to show that even man's brainpower can be explained through the workings of natural selection. To do this, he has to demonstrate "that there is no fundamental difference between man and the higher mammals in their mental faculties." In other words, he must show that while man has *more* intelligence than other animals, he does not have a different *kind* of intelligence. The reason he must prove this is that natural selection produces only slow and gradual improvements. It cannot produce something utterly new and different.

Darwin attacks this problem by showing in great detail that apes and other animals share with man such intellectual traits as boredom and curiosity, the power to pay attention and the ability to remember. Close observers of animal behavior, he says, will notice that when an animal faces some difficulty, it will "pause, deliberate, and resolve." In short, it will reason. The higher animals, in addition, can learn quite quickly from experience. After being cut only once by a sharp tool, Darwin notes, a monkey will quickly learn to handle the tool "with the greatest caution." Many of Darwin's examples of animal intelligence actually came from the various dogs and cats of Down House, which is proof, if proof were needed, that his sharp eyes never rested even while playing with the household pets. Even man's ability to use language has a dim echo in the animal kingdom, he notes, for animals give voice to many kinds of cries and sounds that convey some meaning to their fellow creatures. "May not some unusually wise ape-like animal," asks Darwin, have begun to use such emotional outcries *intentionally* and so have taken the first step toward the development of true speech?

In short, then, man's mental superiority over the apes is enormous, but his intellect is not unique. Other animals share, to a lesser degree, man's capacity for curiosity, wonder, attention, remembering, and reasoning. Since intelligence is obviously useful in the struggle for existence—

A water color by Darwin's cousin Julia Wedgwood conjures up the summers at Down, when the family would sit on the veranda (at right) or in the shade of the lime trees, looking out over the long flower beds full of lilies, sweet-smelling phlox, and blue larkspur.

Applying Darwin's theories to the way man reacts to his society, some sociologists argued that the poor who crammed the slums of the newly industrialized cities were biologically inferior to the rich. Certainly, only the physically fit could survive life in the London street depicted by Gustave Doré.

especially useful to such a relatively weak creature as man —a gradual improvement in intelligence can be produced through the normal operation of natural selection. Therefore, there must in the past have existed numerous apelike ancestors of man who possessed various degrees of intelligence, ranging from the ape level to that of man himself.

It is important to remember that when Darwin wrote *The Descent of Man*, he knew of no fossil remains of such an early apelike man, except for a skull fragment found in Neanderthal, Germany, which scientists thought belonged to some human freak. Since Darwin's day, however, numerous fossil discoveries have overwhelmingly confirmed his theoretical argument for the existence of apelike ancestors of man. In a sense, he predicted what scientists would find, if they looked in the right places and ceased to consider apish skulls as relics of deformed human beings.

Once again, when *The Descent of Man* appeared, Darwin waited anxiously for scorn and abuse to be heaped on his head. Yet, oddly enough, the book failed to arouse any great outburst of fury. "Everybody is talking about it without being shocked," Darwin observed in some surprise to a friend who visited him shortly after its publication.

Twelve years had passed since Darwin had first stunned the world with his theory; it no longer possessed its old power to shock. Not only had science come around to accepting the theory, but men were applying it to a vast range of new subjects as well. Thinkers were beginning to talk of the evolution of law, the evolution of politics, the evolution of the family and of civilization itself. Evolution was becoming a magic word, and Darwin's principle of natural selection was looked upon as the key to understanding the whole universe. Indeed, respectable people now saw a bright side to Darwinism that they had not seen before. Did it not prove, they said, that everything in life automatically becomes better and better?

Millionaire industrialists, such as Andrew Carnegie of Pittsburgh, were enthusiastic about Darwin's theory because it proved, as they saw it, that millionaires were examples of the survival of the fittest in the economic struggle for existence. On what were taken to be Darwinian principles, men now argued that it was bad to help the poor since they were "inferior" creatures who deserved to die in order to make room for their biological superiors. Until it was realized that rich men are not biologically superior but merely the sons of rich fathers, this theory had a powerful effect on social legislation in England and the United States.

Other men were to apply the doctrine of the survival of the fittest to justify war as a benefit to human progress, and still others used it to prove that it was right for more powerful races to exploit the less powerful, just as in nature an improved species will beat out its inferior rivals.

These various doctrines, which go under the heading of "social Darwinism," had nothing to do in any scientific sense with Darwin's biological theory, but they derived much of their force from what was fast becoming the magical authority of "Darwinism." As the American writer Henry Adams remarked at the time: "Evolution from lower to higher raged like an epidemic. Darwin was the greatest of prophets in the most evolutionary of worlds."

Thus, it was no longer easy to abuse Darwin personally, or to treat his discoveries with lighthearted contempt. He was looked upon as one of the great men of the age, and whether men liked his ideas or not, they had respect for his greatness. There were exceptions, of course. The noted novelist Samuel Butler—grandson of Darwin's old schoolmaster of the same name—unleashed an almost insanely bitter attack upon Darwin as one who had stolen the theory of natural selection from others.

The Butler episode had no effect, except perhaps on Butler's reputation, for the public continued to buy Darwin's books almost as readily as if they were novels, and honors streamed into Down House unabated from every corner of the civilized world. By the last years of his life, Darwin could count himself a member of some sixty learned societies in seventeen different countries.

Darwin could hardly keep track of so many societies, partly, no doubt, because he cared so little about honors. Not long after being named an honorary member of the Berlin Academy of Sciences, he characteristically forgot whether he was a member or not and had to ask Hooker if *he* knew. "I distinctly remember," said Darwin, "receiving some diploma." As early as 1864 the great Royal Society had awarded him the Copley Medal, England's highest scientific honor. Queen Victoria, however, never granted him the knighthood normally awarded to outstanding men of science. Perhaps she did not approve of evolution.

Shy and retiring Darwin remained, but he was now so famous that he became the cause of shyness in others. Introduced to Darwin, one young scientist was so frightened that he became tongue-tied, could not speak, and later burst into tears of frustration. When the pioneer American evolutionist Chauncey Wright spent the night at Down

In 1864 Darwin was awarded the Copley Medal, the Royal Society's highest honor. Ironically, however, the society tried to give the impression that it was presented not for The Origin of Species *but for Darwin's other research work.*

House, he was so excited, he said, that he could scarcely sleep all night. By then, Darwin had become virtually a legendary figure and indeed he was the stuff of legends: the quiet, sickly old man who had changed the course of human thought while staying home at Down House.

With the publication of *The Descent of Man*, Darwin felt that his long labors as an evolutionist were complete. "Perhaps I shall never again attempt to discuss theoretical views," he remarked at the time, "I am growing old and weak and no man can tell when his intellectual powers begin to fail." With that resolution, a curious thing now happened to Darwin: his health, after thirty-five years, suddenly and dramatically improved. The mysterious ailment, which had crippled him throughout the long years of labor on his theory, departed with the completion of his work.

Not that Darwin ceased working. To give up research, he found, was impossible. "I cannot endure doing nothing," he wrote to an old friend in 1877, "so I suppose that I shall go on as long as I can without obviously making a fool of myself." There was little danger of Darwin's making a fool of himself in science as he continued his botanical studies with remarkable vigor and with fine fruitful results. Between his seventieth birthday and his death four years later, he published three more scientific books and more than a dozen scientific articles. The last of his books was on the subject of earthworms and how these humble creatures patiently and doggedly change the face of the earth. Earthworms were another of Darwin's scientific hobbyhorses; indeed, there was something of the earthworm about his own patient, painstaking labors. For sheer, dogged devotion to truth and to science, few men can match Darwin's record.

He was approaching the end of the road now, and he decided one day to set down the story of his life for the benefit of his children. He would write it, he said, "as if I were a dead man looking back at my own life. Nor have I found this difficult, for life is nearly over with me."

The little autobiography was Darwin's last chance to take stock of himself, in his modest, straightforward way. There were pleasant things to remember, for Darwin felt deeply that his life had been a happy one. He wrote lovingly of his devotion to Emma, "my greatest blessing," and of her cheerful comfort in the long years of sickness. He recalled

Darwin called the shaded Sand-Walk, opposite, his "thinking path" and walked there daily, with his dog or with the children or friends, such as Hooker, who recalled discussions of "things far off to both mind and eye."

"A man of enlarged curiosity" was Emma's father's apt phrase for the quiet revolutionary, photographed on the Down veranda the year before his death.

148

those far-away days at Cambridge when he rode horses and sang songs as the jolly companion of the merriest undergraduates. So much had changed since then, he reflected, and many of the changes, he had to admit, were sad ones.

He had paid a steep price for his single-minded devotion to science, for the years spent toiling on his great theory had robbed him of many simple pleasures. "For many years I cannot endure to read a line of poetry," he confessed, and Shakespeare, whom in his college days he had loved to read, he now found repulsively dull. "I have also almost lost my taste for pictures or music," he noted sadly, adding that "the loss of these tastes is a loss of happiness." Science, somehow, had withered and narrowed him. "My mind seems to have become a kind of machine for grinding general laws out of large collections of facts."

In a touching finale, Darwin took stock of his abilities and found them unremarkable. He detected, he said, no signs of genius in his modest gifts: "love of science—unbounded patience in long reflecting over any subject—industry in observing and collecting facts—and a fair share of invention as well as of common sense." These qualities, he believed, had helped him most in his work. They are not earth-shaking gifts, yet he had shaken the world with them and Darwin was not sure how he had done it. "With such modest abilities as I possess, it is truly surprising that I should have influenced to a considerable extent the belief of scientific men on some important points."

These are the last words in Darwin's brief autobiography. In December, 1881, he suffered a mild heart seizure on the front doorstep of a friend's London house. The following April at Down, a more severe attack came over him late one night and he fell into a deep faint. When he regained consciousness, after frantic efforts to revive him, he reassured his faithful wife Emma, who was nursing him as she had so many times before: "I am not the least afraid of death. Remember what a good wife you have been to me. Tell all my children to remember how good they have been to me." On the very brink of death he was trying to console his family. That afternoon, April 19, 1882, at the age of seventy-three, Darwin died very peacefully.

One week later, in an elaborate ceremony, the mortal remains of Charles Darwin were laid to rest where so many of England's greatest men lie buried, in Westminster Abbey in London. His coffin was placed, fittingly enough, near that of Sir Isaac Newton, Britain's other immortal discoverer of scientific truth.

HORIZON CARAVEL BOOKS

JOSEPH L. GARDNER, *Editor*

Janet Czarnetzki, *Art Director*

Jean Atcheson, *Associate Editor*

Sandra L. Russell, *Copy Editor*

Jessica R. Baerwald, *Picture Researcher*

Kathleen Fitzpatrick, *Assistant Copy Editor*

Annette Jarman, *Editorial Assistant*

Gertrudis Feliu, *Chief, European Bureau*

Mary Jenkins, *London Correspondent*

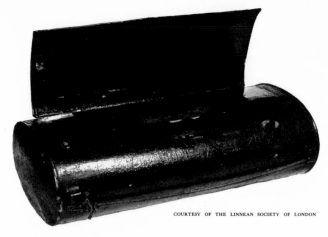

COURTESY OF THE LINNEAN SOCIETY OF LONDON

A battered memento of the Beagle *voyage is this tin box, or vasculum, in which Darwin placed each day's plant specimens.*

ACKNOWLEDGMENTS

The Editors would like to thank the following individuals and organizations for their valuable assistance:

Lady Barlow, Aylesbury, Bucks.

British Museum, Natural History, London—Sir Terence Morrison-Scott, A. J. Macdonald, and their staff

University Library, Cambridge—P. J. Gautrey

Lady Darwin, London

George P. Darwin, Crowthorne, Berks.

The Linnean Society, London—Theodore O'Grady

National Audubon Society, New York—Richard Pasqual

The New York Botanical Garden—Mrs. Lothian Lynas

New York Public Library, Prints Division—Elizabeth Roth

Mrs. Roger Tory Peterson, Old Lyme, Conn.

Photo Researchers, Inc., New York—Mrs. Russ Kinne

Royal College of Surgeons, London: Hunterian Museum—Jessie Dobson; Down House, Kent—Lady Atkins, S. Robinson

Josiah Wedgwood & Sons, Ltd.—Mrs. Moira Gibson

FURTHER READING

For those who would like to know more about Darwin, his family, and his work, the following books are recommended:

Barlow, Nora, ed., *Charles Darwin and the Voyage of the Beagle*. Philosophical Library, 1946.

Darwin, Charles, *Autobiography*, edited by Nora Barlow. Collins, 1958.

———, *The Origin of Species*. Oxford University Press.*

———, *The Voyage of the Beagle*. Dutton, 1960.*

Darwin, Francis, ed., *The Life and Letters of Charles Darwin*, 2 vols. Basic Books, 1959.

Darwin, Francis, and Seward, A. C., eds., *More Letters of Charles Darwin*, 2 vols. Murray, 1903.

De Beer, Gavin, *Charles Darwin: Evolution by Natural Selection*. Doubleday, 1964.*

Eiseley, Loren, *Darwin's Century; Evolution and the Men Who Discovered It*. Doubleday, 1958.

Himmelfarb, Gertrude, *Darwin and the Darwinian Revolution*. Doubleday, 1959.

Huxley, Julian, and Kettlewell, H. B. D., *Charles Darwin and His World*. Viking, 1965.

Irvine, William, *Apes, Angels and Victorians*. McGraw-Hill, 1955.*

Litchfield, Henrietta, ed., *Emma Darwin, Wife of Charles Darwin: A Century of Family Letters*, 2 vols. Murray, 1915.

Moore, Ruth, *Charles Darwin*. Knopf, 1955.

Moore, Ruth, and the Editors of *Life* Magazine, *Evolution*. Time Inc., 1962.

Raverat, Gwen, *Period Piece*. Norton, 1953.

*Also available in paperback.

INDEX

Boldface indicates pages on which maps or illustrations appear

J
B
DARWIN

224591X

Horizon Magazine

Charles Darwin and
the origin of
species

9.89

DATE			

81 02 NOV 30 1978